CONTENTS

GRADE **6**

CHAPTER 1 · Understanding Numbers: Whole Numbers, Decimals

CHAPTER 2 · Using Addition and Subtraction: Whole Numbers, Decimals

i

CHAPTER 3 · Using Multiplication: Whole Numbers, Decimals

CHAPTER 4 · Dividing Whole Numbers

CHAPTER 7 · Adding and Subtracting Fractions and Mixed Numbers

CHAPTER 8 · Multiplying and Dividing Fractions and Mixed Numbers

CHAPTER 9 · Geometry

CHAPTER 10 · Ratio, Proportion, and Percent

CHAPTER 11 · Measurement: Area and Volume

CHAPTER 12 · Probability

CHAPTER 13 · Integers and Coordinate Graphing

Name

FREQUENCY TABLES AND DIAGRAMS

On Your Own   Pair and Share   In a Group

MAGAZINE STAND

Imagine that you are the owner of a magazine stand. You have to place your order for September magazines. Work with a group to determine how many of each magazine you will buy. These two frequency tables should help you.

AUGUST'S SALES

Magazine	Number Sold
Living	70
Outdoor Times	80
Good Looks	38
Dressing Up	27
Kid's World	79
World Explorer	76
Vacations	119
Business Talk	67
Sports Week	72

LAST SEPTEMBER'S SALES

Magazine	Number Sold
Living	55
Outdoor Times	95
Good Looks	76
Dressing Up	51
Kid's World	60
World Explorer	60
Vacations	30
Business Talk	50
Sports Week	70

Here are some things to keep in mind.

1. You are selling more magazines a month now than last year.

2. You should order more copies than you expect to sell. You can return the extras and get most of your money back.

3. Different magazines sell better at different times of the year.

What will you buy for this September? Discuss your reasoning.

Magazine	Expect to Sell	Number to Buy
Living		
Outdoor Times		
Good Looks		
Dressing Up		
Kid's World		
World Explorer		
Vacations		
Business Talk		
Sports World		

MACMILLAN/McGRAW-HILL

Name _____

WHOLE NUMBERS

On Your Own   Pair and Share   In a Group

WAY OUT IN SPACE

In 1772, an astronomer named Bode discovered something about the distances of planets from the Sun. The first seven planets in our solar system follow a number pattern.

1. Each number here is twice as big as the one before. Finish the pattern.

    0   3   6   12   _____   _____   _____   _____

2. Next, add 4 to each number.

    4   7   10   16   _____   _____   _____   _____

Mercury Venus Earth Mars   Jupiter Saturn Uranus

Look at the numbers that correspond to a planet. To find the distance of the planet from the sun, multiply the planet's number by 9,300,000 miles. Use your calculator and what you know about place value to find the product. Start with Earth, number 10.

10 × 9,300,000 = 93,000,000 miles from the Sun

Find the distances for the other planets.

3. Mercury _____

4. Venus _____

5. Earth   9,300,000 × 10 = 93,000,000 miles

6. Mars _____

7. Jupiter _____

8. Saturn _____

9. Uranus _____

What happened to the number between Mars and Jupiter? There is no planet there, but there *is* a group of *asteroids*. These rocky objects may be a planet that exploded. Also, Neptune and Pluto, the most distant planets, do not fit the pattern.

DECIMALS

CROSS THAT BRIDGE

Choose the letter of the correct standard form for each item in the
left column. The letters will spell the answer to this riddle:

What is the shortest bridge in the world?

_____ **1.** six hundred ten
ten thousandths

R 0.061

_____ **2.** sixty-one thousandths

I 0.170

_____ **3.** one hundred seventy
thousandths

F 0.2

_____ **4.** fifty-three thousand,
eleven
hundred-thousandths

O 0.38

_____ **5.** three hundred eighty
thousandths

N 0.20360

_____ **6.** two hundredths

Y 0.7710

_____ **7.** one hundred seventy-
three thousandths

B 0.0610

_____ **8.** two tenths

E 0.771

_____ **9.** seven thousand,
seven hundred
ten ten-thousandths

G 0.380

_____ **10.** thirty-eight hundredths

R 0.2036

_____ **11.** seven hundredths

U 0.07

_____ **12.** two thousand, thirty-six
ten-thousandths

S 0.5301

_____ **13.** twenty thousand, three
hundred sixty
hundred-thousandths

D 0.53011

_____ **14.** twenty hundredths

O 0.173

_____ **15.** five thousand, three
hundred one
ten-thousandths

O 0.20

_____ **16.** seven hundred
seventy-one thousandths

E 0.02

MACMILLAN/McGRAW-HILL

Name _____

On Your Own   Pair and Share   In a Group

DAYS OF OUR LIVES

Study the calendar with your partner. A square four numbers by four numbers has been drawn on the calendar.

Sun.	Mon.	Tues.	Wed.	Thurs.	Fri.	Sat.
	1	2	3	4	5	6
7	8	9	10	11	12	13
14	15	16	17	18	19	20
21	22	23	24	25	26	27
28	29	30	31			

Together, solve the following problems:

1. What is the sum of the numbers along each diagonal?

   _____   _____

2. What is the sum of the four numbers at the corners of the

   square? _____
   The numbers should be equal.

3. How many more four-by-four squares can you find on this calendar? Mark them. You can use different colors if you like.

   _____

4. Find the diagonal sums and the corner sums of each square you found above. Write them here.

   _____

   _____

   _____

MACMILLAN/McGRAW-HILL

Name

PROBLEM SOLVING

WHAT DO YOU THINK?

Work with a group to take a survey of your classmates.

1. Pick a topic that interests your group. Make a list of three or four questions about the topic. Each question should include a list of possible answers to choose from.

   Examples:

   1. What afterschool activity do you like best: sports, reading, television, hobbies?

   2. What is most important to you about an afterschool activity: being with friends, getting exercise, having fun?

   3. Do you have enough time for afterschool activities: yes, no?

Write your group's questions here:

_____

_____

_____

_____

_____

2. Have one person survey the members of your group. Then take turns visiting other groups to get all your classmates' opinions. Record the answers to each question in a frequency table such as this one. Tally all the answers.

	Sports	Reading	Television	Hobbies
Question 1	|||| |||	|||	|||| |	||||

3. Decide how you can best show the results. Do you want to use a graph, a table, or a paragraph? Which one shows your information most clearly? Display your results on the bulletin board.

MACMILLAN/McGRAW-HILL

Name _____

ROUNDING WHOLE NUMBERS AND DECIMALS

On Your Own   Pair and Share   In a Group

THINKING ROUNDLY

Work with a partner to answer the questions.

1. When you are rounding to the nearest ten:

   a. What is the least whole number that rounds to 60? _____

   b. What is the greatest whole number that rounds to 60? _____

   c. How many whole numbers round to 60? _____

2. When you are rounding to the nearest hundred:

   a. What is the least whole number that rounds to 800? _____

   b. What is the greatest whole number that rounds to 800? _____

   c. How many whole numbers round to 800? _____

3. When you are rounding to the nearest thousand:

   a. What is the least whole number that rounds to 3,000? _____

   b. What is the greatest whole number that rounds to 3,000? _____

   c. How many whole numbers round to 3,000? _____

Look for a pattern in Problems 1–3.

4. When you are rounding to the nearest million, how many whole

   numbers round to 4,000,000? _____

5. There are 9,999 whole numbers that round to this number.
   The greatest whole number that rounds to this number is 74,999.

   What is the rounding place? _____

   What is the number? _____

Use the clues. Find the number.

6. This number has three digits. To the nearest tenth, this number

   rounds to 4.2. The sum of the digits is 13. _____

7. To the nearest hundredth, this number rounds to 6.13. The
   thousandths digit is the same as the ones digit. The sum of

   the digits is 15. _____

8. To the nearest thousandth, this number rounds to 0.011. The
   number has five digits. The last three digits are consecutive

   numbers. _____

MACMILLAN/McGRAW-HILL

Name _____

GEARING UP

Look at this diagram of gears in a machine. The arrows show which way the gears are turning. As Gear A turns, the teeth in the gear push on the teeth in Gear B. Gear B turns as well. The arrow shows the way Gear B turns.

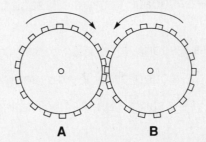

1. Look at this diagram. The arrows show the direction for Gears A, B, and C. Draw arrows to show the direction that Gears D and E are turning.

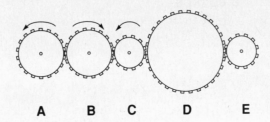

Draw an arrow to show the direction of the last gear in each of these diagrams.

2.

3.

4.

5.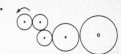

6. Study the number of gears there are in each set above. Is the direction of the last gear the same or different from the first? Can you write a rule telling which way the last gear will turn?

_____

_____

MACMILLAN/McGRAW-HILL

MAKING BAR GRAPHS

On Your Own   Pair and Share   In a Group

AFTER-SCHOOL SPECIALTIES

Five students asked other students in their school "What is your favorite after-school activity?" Here are the answers they got and the number of students who gave each answer.

Aaron's results: 2—chess club, 1—baseball, 1—music lessons, 1—dance lessons, 3—TV

Bill's results: 3—swimming, 1—flute lessons, 2—TV, 2—computer club, 2—reading

Sarah's results: 1—piano lessons, 2—acting club, 2—running, 2—gymnastics

Kevin's results: 2—dance lessons, 1—acting club, 1—swimming, 1—baseball, 1—reading

Jenny's results: 3—reading, 1—chess club, 2—computer club, 1—running, 1—baseball

Make a graph to show this data.

1. Decide how you want to group the answers.
   Make a table showing your categories.

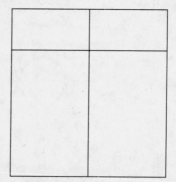

2. Decide on the labels for the two axes and make your graph.

MACMILLAN/McGRAW-HILL

Name _____

PROBLEM SOLVING

On Your Own   Pair and Share   In a Group

HOW GOOD IS YOUR MEMORY?

How long a list of numbers can you remember? Try this experiment with a group of friends.

1. Have one member of the group make up lists of single-digit numbers (from 0 to 9). One list should be 3 numbers long, the next 4 numbers, the next 5 numbers, and so on. The last list should have 15 single-digit numbers. (Numbers may be repeated.)

   Example: 1, 9, 3, 5, 2, 8, 2, 0, 3 (nine numbers)

2. The list maker reads each number list to the other members. As soon as a list is read, each person writes down what he or she can remember of that list.

3. Check what you wrote against the lists. What was the longest list each person could remember? Record the results in a table like this.

Student	Longest List
Jerome	9
Suz	8

4. Discuss the results with your group. What conclusions can be drawn from the experiment? Look at the numbers carefully. What is the average length remembered? Is one length list the most common? Ask the people who remembered the longest lists if they used any tricks to help them.

5. Write a set of statements giving the results of your experiment.

   _____

   _____

   _____

   _____

6. After you have finished, have each group member see if he or she can still remember the numbers in the longest list learned. What do you find?

   _____

   _____

MACMILLAN/McGRAW-HILL

MENTAL MATH: ADDING AND SUBTRACTING

On Your Own   Pair and Share   In a Group

WHEN IN EGYPT

About 5,000 years ago, the ancient Egyptians used pictures, called **hieroglyphics,** to write numbers. The following chart shows some of the pictures and numbers they represented.

Number	Picture
1	|
10	∩
100	ℓ
1,000	⚶
10,000	⌐
100,000	⟟
1,000,000	𓁨

Our numeration system is a place value system. The position of each digit is important. For example, 42 means 4 tens and 2 ones, but 24 means 2 tens and 4 ones. In the Egyptian system, the position of the pictures did not matter.

∩∩ ||| = 10 + 10 + 1 + 1 + 1 = 23

or

||| ∩∩ = 1 + 1 + 1 + 10 + 10 = 23

The values of the pictures are added.

Write each number in our system.

1. ∩∩∩ |||||| _____

2. ℓℓ∩∩ | _____

3. ∩ ℓℓ ⚶⚶ _____

4. ⌐⌐⌐ ⚶⚶⚶⚶⚶ ∩∩∩ ℓℓ || _____

5. 𓁨 ⟟⟟ ⌐⌐⌐⌐⌐ ℓℓℓℓℓℓ ∩∩∩∩∩∩∩ |||||||

_____

Write each number in the Egyptian system.

6. 47 _____

7. 536 _____

8. 2,813 _____

9. 35,000 _____

10. 240,819 _____

11. 1,231,684 _____

12. Does the Egyptian system have a picture that represents zero? Do you think the Egyptians really needed it? Explain.

_____

MACMILLAN/McGRAW-HILL

Name _____

ESTIMATING SUMS AND DIFFERENCES: ROUNDING

On Your Own   Pair and Share   In a Group

TARGET PRACTICE

Look at the target number in each circle. Then choose numbers from the box whose estimated sum *or* difference will be closest to the target. Write the addition or subtraction problem. For Problems 1–5, choose two numbers.

1.

(700)

537	328
89	191

_____

2.

(5,000)

956	8,390
2,738	1,042

_____

3.

(9,000)

1,379	4,897
6,101	3,246

_____

4.

(13,000)

2,871	9,502
12,430	5,984

_____

5.

(20,000)

11,769	4,875
2,958	
40,153	32,066

_____

For Problems 6–7, you may choose more than two numbers and use more than one operation.

6.

(100,000)

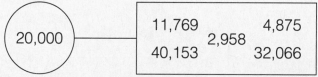

73,459	5,652
8,631	
47,268	19,120

_____

7.

(0)

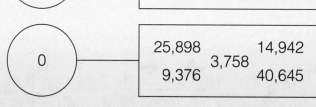

25,898	14,942
3,758	
9,376	40,645

_____

MACMILLAN/McGRAW-HILL

Name _____

PATTERN PICKS

How would you complete the following?

▲ is to △ as ◓ is to ___?___

| A | B | C | D |

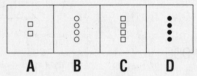

Think: ▲ is the same shape as △ , the first figure has the bottom part shaded, and the second figure has the top part shaded. Look for the same shape as ◓ , but with the top part shaded. The correct answer is D.

Now try this one.

⊟ is to ⊟ as ⦂ is to ___?___

| A | B | C | D |

Which answer is correct? Explain your reasoning. _____

_____

Write the letter of the correct answer.

					A	B	C	D
1.	△ is to ▼ as ⏢ is to ____.				⏢	▶	▼	⟆
2.	⠢ is to ⠔ as ⠿ is to ____.				⣝	⠿	⣏	▫▫▫
3.	⌐ is to ⌐ as ⊢ is to ____.				⌐	⌐	⊔	⊐
4.	△△ △△ is to △△ △▲ as ∘∘ ∘∘ is to ____.				△△ △△	▲▲ ▲▲	∘∘ ∘∘	∘∘ ∘∘
5.	✕✕✕ ✕✕ is to ✕✕ ✕✕ as ∘∘∘ ∘∘∘ is to ____.				∘∘∘ ∘∘	∘∘∘∘ ∘∘∘	✕✕✕ ✕✕	∙∙∙ ∙∙
6.	□ is to ◣ as ○ is to ____.				●	◖	◖	◠
7.	∘∘ ∘∘ is to ⦙ as ⦂ is to ____.				▫	⦙	∘	▪

ADDING AND SUBTRACTING WHOLE NUMBERS

On Your Own   Pair and Share   In a Group

SQUARE DEAL

Fill in the missing numbers in each box so the addition problems are correct across and down. Use a calculator if you wish.

25,145	+		=	57,313
+		+		+
13,481	+	7,519	=	
=		=		=
38,626	+		=	78,313

	+	25,361	=	40,039
+		+		+
	+	10,762	=	
=		=		=
47,569	+		=	83,692

	+	26,108	=	38,306
+		+		+
	+		=	
=		=		=
23,657	+		=	81,592

MACMILLAN/McGRAW-HILL

Name

SOLVING EQUATIONS

On Your Own   Pair and Share   In a Group

EXTREME MEASURES

How do you measure poison ivy?

Solve each equation. Then draw a line to connect each pair of equations that have the same answer. (Use a ruler and draw a line between the dots.) The letters that are not crossed out will answer the riddle.

$n + 7 = 14$ $n =$ ___ •

o   b   d

$n - 3 = 6$ $n =$ ___ •

y

$6 + n = 12$ $n =$ ___ •

a

$3 + n = 8$ $n =$ ___ •   y

$n - 14 = 2$ $n =$ ___ •   i

$n - 5 = 5$ $n =$ ___ •

$n + 6 = 19$ $n =$ ___ • t

r   s

$n - 7 = 4$ $n =$ ___ •

$n + 8 = 16$ $n =$ ___ •

n   f   c

$20 - n = 5$ $n =$ ___ •

$n + 1 = 3$ $n =$ ___ •   r

$n - 8 = 4$ $n =$ ___ • h

e

$20 - n = 16$ $n =$ ___ •

s

$n + 5 = 19$ $n =$ ___ •

$n + 1 = 20$ $n =$ ___ • s

$n - 7 = 14$ $n =$ ___ •   e

$n + 3 = 21$ $n =$ ___ •   t

• $6 - n = 4$ $n =$ ___

• $n + 2 = 14$ $n =$ ___

• $n - 2 = 17$ $n =$ ___

• $n + 3 = 10$ $n =$ ___

• $n - 2 = 8$ $n =$ ___

• $n + 3 = 9$ $n =$ ___

• $n - 1 = 10$ $n =$ ___

• $n + 5 = 10$ $n =$ ___

• $n + 6 = 15$ $n =$ ___

• $n - 4 = 12$ $n =$ ___

• $n + 9 = 17$ $n =$ ___

• $16 - n = 3$ $n =$ ___

• $n + 1 = 16$ $n =$ ___

• $5 - n = 1$ $n =$ ___

• $n - 3 = 11$ $n =$ ___

• $n - 1 = 20$ $n =$ ___

• $n - 4 = 14$ $n =$ ___

MACMILLAN/McGRAW-HILL

Name

PROBLEM SOLVING

On Your Own   Pair and Share   In a Group

MEASURE FOR MEASURE

Can you judge how long a room is just by looking at it? Can you guess the weight of a package just by picking it up?

You can get better at estimating lengths and weights by practicing. Work with a partner. You will need a ruler or yardstick and a scale.

1. Start by adding to this list of things to measure or weigh in your classroom.

Lengths to Measure	Estimate	Things to Weigh	Estimate
classroom wall pencil		math book telephone	

2. Record your estimates. Don't look at your partner's estimates until you are finished with your own.

Now work with your partner to measure and weigh the things on your lists. Compare your estimates with the actual results.

3. How close were you? _____

4. What measurements give you the most trouble?

    _____

5. Which kinds of measurements do you overestimate? Which do you underestimate?

    _____

    _____

6. Now make a new list of things to measure. Use what you learned to try to make better estimates. Then measure again.

Lengths to Measure	Estimate	Things to Weigh	Estimate
width of hallway paper		phone book piece of fruit	

7. Did your estimating improve?

    _____

TOURIST TRAP

The sixth-grade class at Walker School is going to visit Center City. They will leave from school at 7:00 A.M., take a bus to the city, and then spend the day. They must return to the school by 6:00 P.M.

Make a schedule for the day. Be sure there is time to get to and do each activity. You don't have to do it all. Don't forget lunch!

FACTS ABOUT CENTER CITY

You can schedule more time for any activity than is listed here, but do not schedule less. Allow $\frac{1}{2}$ hour to get to a new place.

- Trip to any location in Center City takes 1 hour.

- Center City Zoo opens 10:00 A.M. Has a cafeteria. Allow at least 2 hours to see the zoo.

- Art museum opens 9:00 A.M. Has a cafeteria. $1\frac{1}{2}$ hour tour can be arranged for any time.

- Tours of an automobile factory are at 10:00 A.M., 12 noon, 2:00 P.M., and 4:00 P.M. Tour takes 1 hour.

- Drive around the city to see many buildings and neighborhoods takes $1\frac{1}{2}$ hours.

- Next to the zoo is a park with a lake to swim in. You can walk to it. Has a picnic ground.

- The tallest building in town is the Foster Tower. Opens at 8:00 A.M. You can see the view in $\frac{1}{2}$ hour.

- Special children's show at the local playhouse will be held at 1:00 P.M. and 3:00 P.M. Has a cafeteria. Show lasts $1\frac{1}{2}$ hours.

STARTING TIME	ENDING TIME	ACTIVITY
7:00 A.M.		Take bus to Center City.
	6:00 P.M.	Return to Walker School.

MACMILLAN/McGRAW-HILL

Name

ADDING AND SUBTRACTING DECIMALS

On Your Own   Pair and Share   In a Group

HUNT FOR THE MISSING NUMBERS

Fill in the missing numbers in these addition and subtraction problems. Use any method you wish.

1.
```
  2 2 . _ 1 3
+ _ _ . 1 2 _
-------------
  5 6 . 9 3 7
```

2.
```
  _ 3 _ . 4 5
+ 2 _ 2 . 0 _
-------------
  3 8 5 . 4 6
```

3.
```
  3 2 . 7 _ 1
- _ 0 . 6 0 _
-------------
  2 _ . 1 0 1
```

4.
```
  _ 6 . 8 9 1
-   8 . _ _ 0
-------------
    8 . 4 4 1
```

5.
```
  1 _ . 7 6 1
+ 3 8 . _ 2 _
-------------
  5 3 . 9 9 0
```

6.
```
  4 _ _ . _ 1
+ 2 3 0 . 8 1
-------------
  7 0 2 . 0 2
```

7.
```
  1 5 . _ 2 3
- _ 2 . 9 1 _
-------------
    2 . 3 0 5
```

8.
```
  _ 4 . _ 7
- 3 8 . 8 _
-----------
  1 5 . 7 8
```

9.
```
  5 . 0 2 8
+ 5 . 9 _ _
-----------
1 _ . 0 2 7
```

10.
```
  6 . _ 4 _
+ _ . 9 1 5
-----------
1 0 . 0 6 2
```

11.
```
  _ 8 . 1 0
- 6 _ . 8 _
-----------
    8 . 2 1
```

12.
```
  3 . _ _ 1
- 1 . 9 2 8
-----------
  _ . 1 6 _
```

13.
```
  5 . 6 _ 1
  3 . _ 0 1
+ _ . 8 3 _
-----------
1 3 . 6 1 5
```

14.
```
  2 3 . 0 _ _
   6 . 6 1 0
+ 1 _ . _ 3 2
-------------
  4 8 . 1 5 4
```

MACMILLAN/McGRAW-HILL

Name _____

METRIC UNITS OF LENGTH: PERIMETER

On Your Own   Pair and Share   In a Group

RULERS OF SPACE

Imagine that creatures from the planet Xercon have come to visit Earth. They tell us some facts about the Xerconian system of measurement. Use these facts to figure out their system. Fill out the table at the bottom of the page.

1. The basic unit of length is the Draco.

2. A Markel is equal to 16 Bacos.

3. A Zismo is equal to 8 Markels.

4. A Markel is 8 Dracos.

5. A Baco is 2 Hubrics.

6. A Hubric is $\frac{1}{2}$ Baco.

XERCONIAN MEASUREMENT–LENGTH

Units of Length From Shortest to Longest	How Many Dracos Is This Unit?
Hubric	
Baco	
Draco	
Markel	
Zismo	

Answer the following questions.
Use your chart to help you.

1. How many Bacos equal 3 Markels? _____

2. How many Hubrics equal $\frac{1}{2}$ Zismo? _____

3. How many Markels are equal to 64 Hubrics? _____

Work with a group of friends.
Try making up your own system of measurement units.
Then write some questions based on your system. Ask another group to answer your questions.

MACMILLAN/McGRAW-HILL

PROBLEM SOLVING

On Your Own   Pair and Share   In a Group

PRETTY PICTURES

Teams

Play this game with a partner and another team of two students. It's very important that one person on each team *not* see this page before you begin.

Object

On each team, one person will give directions to a partner. This person will tell the partner how to draw each of the figures on this page. After all four figures have been drawn, compare the results. Which drawings look most like the figures on this page? The team with the most accurate drawings is the winner.

Rules

The partner who is drawing should sit at a desk. The partner who is giving directions should sit across the desk and hold the page so it can't be seen.

The person giving directions can use any words to describe what to do, but cannot use gestures or point to anything. The person drawing cannot ask any questions. He or she should just follow directions.

Figures

1.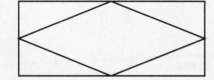

2.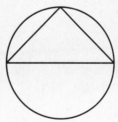

3.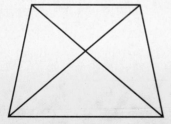

4.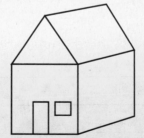

Macmillan/McGraw-Hill, MATHEMATICS IN ACTION
Grade 6, Chapter 2, Lesson 12, pages 70–71

Name _____

READING AND INTERPRETING LINE GRAPHS

On Your Own   Pair and Share   In a Group

READING BETWEEN THE LINES

Work with a partner taking turns doing the activity and answering the questions.

The town drama club asks you for help. Fewer people are coming to see their plays than before. They give you the two graphs shown here. Can you help them figure out what is going on?

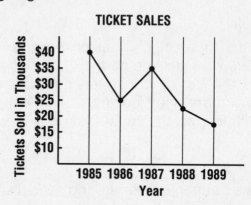

1. First, write some of the facts you see on the Ticket Sales graph.

_____

_____

2. Then write some of the facts you see on the Ticket Prices graph.

_____

_____

3. Now compare the two graphs for each year. Write some of the conclusions you can draw.

_____

_____

_____

4. What do you think the drama club should do?

_____

_____

_____

Name

On Your Own   Pair and Share   In a Group

COMMON QUALITIES

Here are two sets of numbers. Set A has odd numbers. Set B has even numbers.

A

1 3 45 9 11
25 7 87 99

B

2 66 4 82
6 10 18 48

Here the two sets overlap. The numbers that fit in set C where the sets overlap have something else in common. They are under 20. One set is even and under 20; one set is odd and under 20.

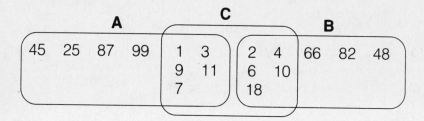

Look at each of these diagrams. Write what the numbers in each set have in common.

1.

A

0.3 1.7 3.2
0.5 0.08 41.62
9.1

B

1 12 25
108 15
17 16

2.

A

15 91
27 1 4
16 46

B

101 197
104 125
106 118

3.

A

15 25
35 5
65

C

105
115
175

156 126
106
186

B

6 36
76 26
16

MACMILLAN/McGRAW-HILL

WHO'S WHO?

Anne, Beth, Charles, and David go to four different schools. The schools are Lincoln, Washington, Cleveland, and Roosevelt. Write the school that each student goes to. Use the clues below to help you.

Anne _____

Beth _____

Charles _____

David _____

CLUES

1. The person who goes to Washington is a boy.

2. Charles used to go to Washington, but he changed schools this year.

3. Anne's school played softball against Roosevelt last month.

4. The student at Roosevelt is a girl.

5. Charles's cousin lives on the other side of town and goes to Lincoln.

You might find it helpful to fill in this chart as you get information about the students. Write X for no and √ for yes.

	Lincoln	Washington	Cleveland	Roosevelt
Anne				
Beth				
Charles				
David				

MACMILLAN/McGRAW-HILL

ESTIMATING PRODUCTS

On Your Own   Pair and Share   In a Group

AND THE QUESTION IS...

Here are some answers. Put a check mark next to each problem
that would give you that answer. (More than one problem may
lead to the answer.) Then write another problem that would give
you the same answer.

1. A good estimate is 6,000.

109×6
199×3
601×12

Your problem _____

2. A good estimate is 2,400.

200×80
215×12
578×4

Your problem _____

3. A good estimate is 600.

16×3
16×39
32×19

Your problem _____

4. A good estimate is 20,000.

514×39
50×43
5×303

Your problem _____

5. A good estimate is 7,000.

69×99
25×278
139×49

Your problem _____

6. A good estimate is 60,000.

$14,000 \times 4$
600×90
250×20

Your problem _____

7. A good estimate is 500,000.

$25,000 \times 45$
$24,999 \times 19$
$15 \times 3,256$

Your problem _____

8. A good estimate is 2,000,000.

495×520
$5,103 \times 389$
$11,000 \times 1,800$

Your problem _____

MACMILLAN/McGRAW-HILL

Name

MULTIPLYING

On Your Own   Pair and Share   In a Group

SCRAMBLED NUMBERS

Use the numbers in the box to write the factors and the product
for each multiplication problem.

1.

| 2 |
| 1 |
| 3 |

$$
\begin{array}{r}
9\ \_\ \_ \\
\times\qquad 3 \\
\hline
2,76\_
\end{array}
$$

2.

| 8 |
| 1 |
| 3 |

$$
\begin{array}{r}
4\ \_\ 7 \\
\times\qquad \_ \\
\hline
3,3\_6
\end{array}
$$

3.

| 7 |
| 3 |
| 0 |

$$
\begin{array}{r}
4\ \_\ 8 \\
\times\qquad 9 \\
\hline
\_,6\_2
\end{array}
$$

4.

| 0 | 1 |
| 0 | 0 |

$$
\begin{array}{r}
1,\_2\_ \\
\times\qquad 8 \\
\hline
8,\_6\_
\end{array}
$$

5.

| 6 | 2 |
| 5 | 5 |

$$
\begin{array}{r}
2,\_7\ 1 \\
\times\qquad \_ \\
\hline
1\_,4\_6
\end{array}
$$

6.

0	4
0	5
2	

$$
\begin{array}{r}
\_,\_\_5 \\
\times\qquad 7 \\
\hline
\_8,03\_
\end{array}
$$

7.

2	0
1	8
5	

$$
\begin{array}{r}
9\ \_\ \_ \\
\times\qquad \_ \\
\hline
1,\_3\_
\end{array}
$$

8.

1	6
3	3
2	8

$$
\begin{array}{r}
7\ \_\ \_ \\
\times\qquad \_ \\
\hline
2,\_\_\_
\end{array}
$$

MACMILLAN/McGRAW-HILL

MULTIPLYING GREATER NUMBERS

On Your Own   Pair and Share   In a Group

SERIOUS SERIES

These numbers follow a pattern. Each number is 12 times the number before it.

> 3   36   432   5,184

The next two numbers in the series are 62,208 (5,184 × 12) and 746,496 (62,208 × 12).

For each series, describe the pattern. Then fill in the next two numbers in each series. Use a calculator to help you. (<u>Hint</u>: Remember, not every series uses multiplication or only one operation.)

1. 4 64 1,024 _____ _____   _____

2. 5 10 15 20 25 _____ _____   _____

3. 3 51 867 _____ _____   _____

4. 23 184 1,472 11,776 _____ _____   _____

5. 3 8 40 45 225 230 _____ _____   _____

6. 6 13 91 98 686 693 _____ _____   _____

7. 12 10 660 658 43,428 _____ _____   _____

8. 19 10 90 81 729 _____ _____   _____

9. 124 248 496 992 _____ _____   _____

10. 375 75 600 300 2,400 _____ _____   _____

11. Write a series using a multiplication pattern. Give it to a friend to solve.

_____

12. Write a series with a pattern that uses addition *or* subtraction and multiplication. Give it to a friend to solve.

_____

MACMILLAN/McGRAW-HILL

Name _____

EXPONENTS

On Your Own   Pair and Share   In a Group

EXPONENTIALLY SPEAKING

Remember that you can use exponents to show multiplication when all the factors are the same.

$$5 \times 5 \times 5 \times 5 = 5^4$$

Now study the multiplication shown below.

$$(3 \times 3 \times 3) \qquad \times \qquad (3 \times 3) \qquad = \qquad 3 \times 3 \times 3 \times 3 \times 3$$

$$27 \qquad \times \qquad 9 \qquad = \qquad 243$$

Write the exponents and the product in each problem. Then check that

1.

$$
\begin{array}{rcl}
3 \times 3 \times 3 & = & 3^{\square} \\
\times \quad 3 \times 3 & = & \times 3^{\square} \\
\hline
3 \times 3 \times 3 \times 3 \times 3 & = & 3^{\square}
\end{array}
$$

$$
\begin{array}{r}
2\;7 \\
\times \;\square\;\square \\
\hline
\square\;\square\;\square
\end{array}
$$

2.

$$
\begin{array}{rcl}
4 \times 4 & = & 4^{\square} \\
\times \quad 4 \times 4 \times 4 \times 4 & = & \times 4^{\square} \\
\hline
4 \times 4 \times 4 \times 4 \times 4 \times 4 & = & 4^{\square}
\end{array}
$$

$$
\begin{array}{r}
\square\;\square \\
\times \;\square\;\square\;\square \\
\hline
\square,\square\;\square\;\square
\end{array}
$$

3.

$$
\begin{array}{rcl}
2 \times 2 \times 2 & = & 2^{\square} \\
\times \quad 2 \times 2 \times 2 & = & \times 2^{\square} \\
\hline
2 \times 2 \times 2 \times 2 \times 2 \times 2 & = & 2^{\square}
\end{array}
$$

$$
\begin{array}{r}
\square \\
\times \;\square \\
\hline
\square\;\square
\end{array}
$$

4. Can you write a rule that tells how to multiply two or more numbers in exponent form? What must be true about the base of each exponential number?

_____

_____

Use your rule to write the answer to these problems. Then write the factors and products in standard form. Check that the products are correct. Use a calculator.

5. $4^2 \times 4^2 =$ _____   _____

6. $7^4 \times 7^3 =$ _____   _____

7. $12^3 \times 12^2 =$ _____   _____

8. $2^2 \times 2^3 \times 2^4 =$ _____   _____

MACMILLAN/McGRAW-HILL

Name

PROBLEM SOLVING

STEP BY STEP

Juanita buys decorations for a party. She buys 10 large balloons at $.98 each and 7 rolls of streamers at $1.09 each. How much does she spend in all?

It takes several steps to solve the problem:

Step 1 $10 \times \$.98 = \$9.80$

Step 2 $7 \times \$1.09 = \$7.63$

Step 3 $\$9.80 + \$7.63 = \$17.43$

1. Work with a group to create a set of problems that require *two or more* steps to solve. Each person in the group should write one problem about planning a party.

Pick from this list of ideas or use your own. Make up names and numbers for each problem.

- Buying food for the party.
- Finding out how many feet of streamers are needed for decorations.
- Finding the total number of people coming to the party.
- Deciding how much flour to buy to make cakes and cookies.
- Figuring how much money is left after buying food and drink.
- Finding the total cost of paper plates, cups, and plastic spoons.

Your problem:

_____

_____

_____

_____

Answer: _____

2. After the problems are written, review all the problems as a group to be sure they make sense. Check to see that the answers are correct.

3. Trade your problems with another group. See which group can solve the other's set of problems faster.

MACMILLAN/McGRAW-HILL

Name _____

MENTAL MATH: MULTIPLYING DECIMALS

On Your Own   Pair and Share   In a Group

MULTIPLICATION MAKES MAGIC

1. Multiply. Write each product in the box below that has the same letter as the problem. Leave **o** and **p** blank for now.

a. 0.072 × 10 _____   b. 0.0036 × 100 _____

c. 0.012 × 100 _____   d. 0.0018 × 1,000 _____

e. 0.108 × 10 _____   f. 0.0192 × 100 _____

g. 0.0006 × 1,000 _____   h. 0.048 × 10 _____

i. 0.0084 × 100 _____   j. 0.024 × 10 _____

k. 0.000132 × 10,000 _____   l. 0.00168 × 1,000 _____

m. 0.0144 × 100 _____   n. 0.000156 × 10,000 _____

o. _____   p. _____

2. In a magic square, the sum of each row, column, and diagonal should be the same. Fill in the two missing boxes so that you have a magic square. Then write multiplication problems for letters **o** and **p** above.

a.	b.	c.	d.
e.	f.	g.	h.
i.	j.	k.	l.
m.	n.	o.	p.

The magic sum is _____

Name _____

CLASSROOM CAPER

What is the best arrangement for a classroom? Where should the desks go? Where should the bookcases be?

Here is a grid showing a classroom that is 20 feet by 35 feet. Plan a layout for a classroom that has 20 desks and chairs and as many bookcases as you like. Draw each desk, chair, and bookcase on the grid. Below the classroom grid are samples to show you how large these items should be.

When you plan your layout, think about whether students will work alone or in groups. Think about how you can use the furniture to divide the space into smaller areas. Be sure there is enough room to walk. Discuss your layout with some friends.

CLASSROOM

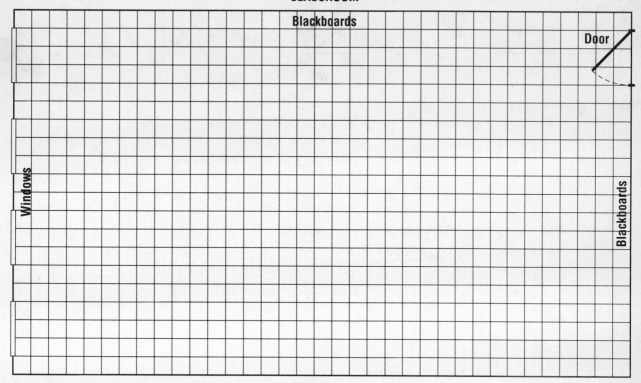

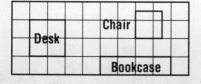

MACMILLAN/McGRAW-HILL

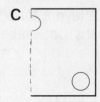

Name _____

On Your Own   Pair and Share   In a Group

FOLD ON THE DOTTED LINE

1. Imagine that the first figure on the left is a sheet of paper with holes punched in it. It will be folded along the dotted line. Which drawing shows how it will look when folded?

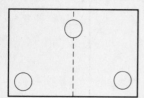   **A** 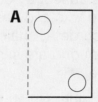   **B** 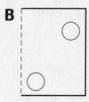   **C**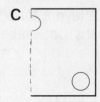

2. Which drawing shows how the paper on the left will look when it is folded?

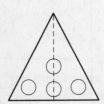   **A**    **B**    **C**

3. Draw a picture to show how this paper will look when it is folded.

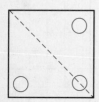

The papers below have been folded on the dotted line. Draw how each paper will look when it is opened up.

4.   5.

6.

Name _____

MULTIPLYING DECIMALS

On Your Own   Pair and Share   In a Group

PUZZLING NUMBERS

Multiply. Then find each answer in the grid below. Write the word
that matches each number in the grid.

1. is

$$
\begin{array}{r}
4.5 \\
\times\,0.09 \\
\hline
\end{array}
$$

2. funny

$$
\begin{array}{r}
9.98 \\
\times\,11.36 \\
\hline
\end{array}
$$

3. both

$$
\begin{array}{r}
0.89 \\
\times\,4.39 \\
\hline
\end{array}
$$

4. have

$$
\begin{array}{r}
55.1 \\
\times\,0.15 \\
\hline
\end{array}
$$

5. A

$$
\begin{array}{r}
3.44 \\
\times\,0.08 \\
\hline
\end{array}
$$

6. story

$$
\begin{array}{r}
7.7 \\
\times\,0.578 \\
\hline
\end{array}
$$

7. pencil

$$
\begin{array}{r}
5.6 \\
\times\,0.996 \\
\hline
\end{array}
$$

8. They

$$
\begin{array}{r}
0.45 \\
\times\,0.566 \\
\hline
\end{array}
$$

9. a

$$
\begin{array}{r}
4.781 \\
\times\quad 3.5 \\
\hline
\end{array}
$$

10. like

$$
\begin{array}{r}
11.41 \\
\times\quad 0.55 \\
\hline
\end{array}
$$

11. a

$$
\begin{array}{r}
0.981 \\
\times\quad 0.33 \\
\hline
\end{array}
$$

12. point

$$
\begin{array}{r}
0.877 \\
\times\quad 0.29 \\
\hline
\end{array}
$$

0.2752	5.5776	0.405	6.2755
_____	_____	_____	_____
16.7335	113.3728	4.4506	0.2547
_____	_____	_____	_____
3.9071	8.265	0.32373	0.25433
_____	_____	_____	_____

MACMILLAN/McGRAW-HILL

Macmillan/McGraw-Hill, MATHEMATICS IN ACTION
Grade 6, Chapter 3, Lesson 11, pages 112–113

Name

MORE MULTIPLYING DECIMALS

On Your Own   Pair and Share   In a Group

CASTING OUT NINES

You may have used casting out nines to check your answers in addition. It works in multiplication problems too.

Cross out all the nines in each factor and the product. Then cross out the digits that add to nine.

Add the digits across each factor and the product. If they add to 10 or more, add the digits again. Always cast out nines.

0.334	→	$3 + 3 + 4 = 10$	→	$1 + 0 = 1$
$\times$ 1.87	→		→	7
0.62458	→	$6 + 2 + 8 = 16$	→	$1 + 6 = 7$

Multiply the results for two factors. Do they equal the result for the product? If they do, the multiplication is probably right. If they don't, the multiplication is probably wrong. Here the multiplication is probably right. (You can also estimate as an additional check.)

0.334	→	1	
$\times$ 1.87	→	$\times 7$	(Estimate: $2 \times 0.3 = 0.6$)
0.62458	→	7	

Multiply. Then try casting out nines to check the answer.

1. 4.35
    × 1.91

2. 3.67
    × 1.3

3. 9.14
    × 3.2

4. 25.06
    × 2.25

5. 0.074
    × 0.83

6. 0.277
    × 0.33

MACMILLAN/McGRAW-HILL

PROBLEM SOLVING

On Your Own   Pair and Share   In a Group

FACT DETECTIVES

You can't solve each of these problems until you find a missing fact. Work with a partner. Use an almanac or other source. Then solve each problem.

1. Mt. McKinley in Alaska is 5,826 feet higher than Mt. Whitney in California. How high is Mt. McKinley?

   Missing fact: _____

   Answer: _____

2. The melting point of silver is 102° less than the melting point of gold. What is the melting point of silver?

   Missing fact: _____

   Answer: _____

3. The Cape Cod Canal in Massachusetts is 27 miles shorter than the Panama Canal. How long is the Cape Cod Canal?

   Missing fact: _____

   Answer: _____

4. When Mt. St. Helens volcano in Washington State erupted in 1980, people compared it with the famous eruption of Mt. Vesuvius in Roman times. How many years before the Mt. St. Helens eruption did this take place?

   Missing fact: _____

   Answer: _____

5. A gallon in the United States is a smaller unit of measurement than a gallon in Great Britain. The number of cubic inches in a U.S. gallon is 46.42 inches less than a British Imperial gallon. How many cubic inches are there in an English gallon?

   Missing fact: _____

   Answer: _____

6. Lake Superior, the largest lake in the world, is 43 miles longer than Lake Michigan. How long is Lake Superior?

   Missing fact: _____

   Answer: _____

MACMILLAN/McGRAW-HILL

Name _____

AREAS OF RECTANGLES

On Your Own   Pair and Share   In a Group

ODD AREAS

The area of a figure is the number of square units that can fit inside it. This figure has an area of 6 square units.

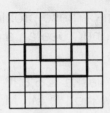

Finish each of these figures so they have the area shown. The figure must fit on the grid.

1. 6 square units

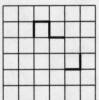   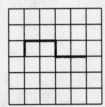

2. 8 square units

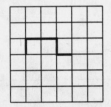   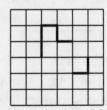

3. 10 square units

   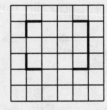

4. 8 square units

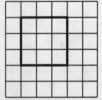   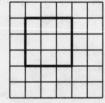

5. 12 square units

   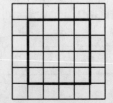

MACMILLAN/McGRAW-HILL

Name _____

VOLUMES OF RECTANGULAR PRISMS

On Your Own   Pair and Share   In a Group

PATTERN MAKING

Can you make space figures out of a flat piece of paper? Look at the drawing of a cube on the left. The pattern on the right can be folded on the lines to make a cube.

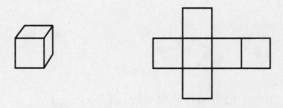

1. Draw the pattern on another piece of paper. Make it larger. Cut it and fold it to make a cube. (You'll need a pencil, ruler, scissors, and tape.)

Can you make these two figures from a piece of paper? Draw the patterns you used in the space at the right.

2.

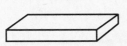

MACMILLAN/McGRAW-HILL

3.

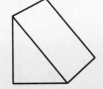

RELATING MULTIPLICATION AND DIVISION

On Your Own   Pair and Share   In a Group

THE BLACK BOX

The black box contains a rule that changes numbers. Look at the numbers on the left. Then see what they become when they come out of the black box.

```
16 ──────┐    ┌──→ 48
27 ──────┤ ██ ├──→ 81
61 ──────┘    └──→ 183
```

The rule inside the black box must be to multiply the number that goes in by 3.

Look at each of these examples. Write the rule. Then write the output for the last number. The rules may have more than one step, such as multiply by 3 and add 1.

1.
```
7                    105
1    ──→ ☐ ──→       15
12                   180
14                   ___
```
Rule: _____

2.
```
2                    5
6    ──→ ☐ ──→       13
10                   21
29                   ___
```
Rule: _____

3.
```
15                   38
3    ──→ ☐ ──→       14
10                   28
17.5                 ___
```
Rule: _____

4.
```
1                    11
2    ──→ ☐ ──→       16
10                   56
193                  ___
```
Rule: _____

5.
```
20                   6
100  ──→ ☐ ──→       26
28                   8
1.2                  ___
```
Rule: _____

Name _____

On Your Own   Pair and Share   In a Group

CODE BREAKER

The letters A to J stand for the numbers 0 to 9. Two letters stand
for a two-digit number. Look at the problems below. They will help
you break the code. Write the number that each letter stands for.

A	B	C	D	E	F	G	H	I	J
__	__	__	__	__	__	__	__	__	__

$$\begin{array}{r} B \\ \times A \\ \hline B \end{array}$$

$$\begin{array}{r} J \\ \times I \\ \hline I \end{array}$$

$$\begin{array}{r} I \\ + D \\ \hline D \end{array}$$

$$\begin{array}{r} F \\ + F \\ \hline AI \end{array}$$

$$\begin{array}{r} F \\ - A \\ \hline E \end{array}$$

$$\begin{array}{r} F \\ \times C \\ \hline AI \end{array}$$

$$\begin{array}{r} C \\ + E \\ \hline J \end{array}$$

$$C\overline{)AJ}^{\,D}$$

$$J + A = B$$

$$E \times H = AC$$

$$F + C + C = G$$

NUMBERS AND LETTERS

In our number system, every place is ten times the value of the place to the right. Our system is called *base ten.*

You may have worked with base two or other number systems. Computer programmers often use base sixteen. It is called *hexadecimal notation.* Every place is 16 times the place to the right. In hexadecimal notation, the number 1,111 means

4,096s	256s	16s	1s
1	1	1	1

This number is
$$1 \times 4{,}096 = 4{,}096$$
$$1 \times \phantom{4{,}}256 = \phantom{4{,}}256$$
$$1 \times \phantom{4{,}2}16 = \phantom{4{,}2}16$$
$$1 \times \phantom{4{,}25}1 = \underline{\phantom{4{,}25}1}$$
$$4{,}369$$

In our system, you regroup when you reach ten in any place. In hexadecimal notation, you regroup when you reach 16. How do you show values greater than 9? You use letters.

Hexadecimal values:

Base Ten	0 – 9	10	11	12	13	14	15
Base Sixteen	0 – 9	A	B	C	D	E	F

Translate these hexadecimal numbers into base ten.

1. 11 _____

2. 301 _____

3. A _____

4. A0 _____

5. 10,000 _____

6. 20E _____

7. 11A1 _____

8. D1B _____

Translate these base ten numbers into hexadecimal numbers.

9. 19 _____

10. 31 _____

11. 517 _____

12. 49 _____

13. 4,109 _____

14. 65,568 _____

15. 4,080 _____

16. 100 _____

MACMILLAN/McGRAW-HILL

Name

DIVIDING BY ONE-DIGIT NUMBERS

On Your Own   Pair and Share   In a Group

PUZZLING PATTERN

Write the missing numbers and signs. Use a calculator to help you. (There is more than one right answer in some places.)

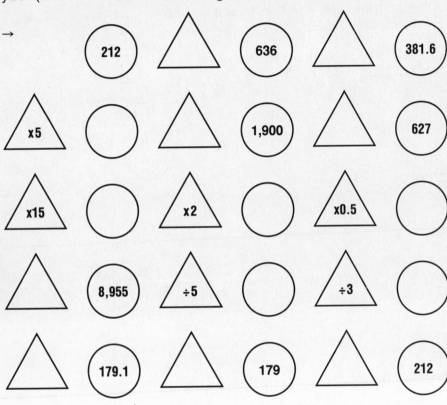

Create your own pattern puzzle. Give it to a friend to solve.

Macmillan/McGraw-Hill, MATHEMATICS IN ACTION
Grade 6, Chapter 4, Lesson 4, pages 144–145

MACMILLAN/McGRAW-HILL

DIVIDING BY TWO-DIGIT NUMBERS

On Your Own   Pair and Share   In a Group

MISSING DIGITS

Which state is nicknamed the *Show Me State*? To find out, write the missing digits in each division problem. Then find the quotients below and write the correct letter in each space.

1.

S

```
        1 2 R □□
   3 2)3 9 8
       □□
       □□
       □ 4
       □□
```

2.

O

```
         1 5
   5 □)8 5 □
     5 □
     □ 8 □
     2 8 □
```

3.

U

```
       2 □ R 7
  □□)9 0 7
     9 0
       □
       □
       7
```

4.

I

```
        8 □ R 7
  9 5)□□ 6 □
      7 6 0
      7 6 □
      7 6 0
          7
```

5.

M

```
       3 □ R 11
  1 □)5 □ 9
     5 1
     7 9
     □□
     1 1
```

6.

R

```
        1 □ R 4
  □ 2)1 3 □ 8
     □ 2
     5 7 8
     5 7 4
         4
```

The <u>Show Me State</u> is _____ _____ _____ _____ _____ _____ _____ _____

34R11   88R7   12R14   12R14   15   20R7   17R4   88R7

MACMILLAN/McGRAW-HILL

Name _____

On Your Own   Pair and Share   In a Group

PUZZLING NUMBERS

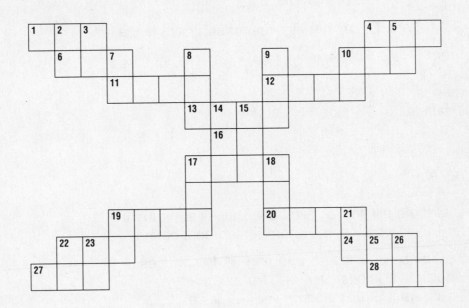

ACROSS

1. $10,900 \div 25$

4. ___ $\div 7 = 79$

6. ___ $\div 4 = 157$

10. ___ $\div 2 = 52$

11. ___ $\div 60 = 26$

12. ___ $\div 47 = 58$

13. ___ $\div 88 = 52$

16. ___ $\div 7 = 8$

17. ___ $\div 4 = 711$

19. ___ $\div 25 = 200$

20. ___ $\div 82 = 28$

22. $696 \div 6$

24. ___ $\div 4 = 131$

27. ___ $\div 7 = 94$

28. ___ $\div 10 = 23$

DOWN

2. $540 \div 15$

3. $5,084 \div 82$

4. $450 \div 9$

5. $5,292 \div$ ___ $= 98$

7. $2,025 \div 25$

8. ___ $\div 151 = 4$

9. $630 \div 5$

10. $256 \div 16$

14. ___ $\div 62 = 9$

15. ___ $\div 191 = 4$

17. $1,600 \div 8$

18. $1,206 \div 3$

19. $448 \div 8$

21. $520 \div 8$

22. $1,380 \div 92$

23. $36 \div 2$

25. $990 \div 45$

26. $2,365 \div 55$

MACMILLAN/McGRAW-HILL

PROBLEM SOLVING

On Your Own   Pair and Share   In a Group

THE CHECK, PLEASE

Work with a partner to answer the questions below.

Andy, Beth, Chita, and Danny eat at a restaurant. Here is the bill.

6 burgers	$14.34
6 juices	$ 5.34
2 puddings	$ 3.78
2 fruit salads	$ 4.50
2 french fries	$ 2.38
2 milks	$ 1.98
TOTAL	$33.32

They want to split the bill so that each one pays just for the items
he or she ate. This is what each of them remembers eating:

Andy	2 burgers	2 juices	1 pudding	1 french fries
Beth	1 burger	2 juices	1 milk	1 french fries
Chita	2 burgers	1 fruit salad	1 milk	1 juice
Danny	2 burgers	1 fruit salad	1 pudding	1 juice

1. What is the cost of each individual item on the bill?

   _____

   _____

2. How much should each pay?

   Andy _____   Beth _____

   Chita _____   Danny _____

3. What is the total? _____

4. Your total should be higher than the bill. One reason is that
   one of the students remembered incorrectly what he or she ate.

   What is it? _____

5. Something else may be wrong. Check the total bill.

   What is the correct amount? _____

6. What do you think each student should pay?

   Andy _____   Beth _____

   Chita _____   Danny _____

Macmillan/McGraw-Hill, MATHEMATICS IN ACTION
Grade 6, Chapter 4, Lesson 7, pages 150–151

MACMILLAN/McGRAW-HILL

DIVIDING GREATER NUMBERS

On Your Own   Pair and Share   In a Group

SQUARE OFF

Use these numbers to fill in the square so that the division
problems are correct across each row and down each column.
One row is already filled in for you.

952   68   8,092   238   64,736   34

	÷		=	
÷	▓	÷	▓	÷
	÷		=	
=	▓	=	▓	=
8	÷	4	=	2

Fill in the numbers in this square.

7   4,590   595   1,080   140   20   642,600   85   54

	÷		=	
÷	▓	÷	▓	÷
	÷		=	
=	▓	=	▓	=
	÷		=	

MACMILLAN/McGRAW-HILL

MULTIPLICATION AND DIVISION EQUATIONS

On Your Own   Pair and Share   In a Group

DEEP DEPTHS

Mt. Everest is the highest point on the earth. What is the lowest point? To find out, solve each equation. Write the letter above each question in the space below that matches n. (Write the letter everywhere there is a matching number.)

B
$6n = 36$

_____

E
$n \div 4 = 4$

_____

D
$7n = 49$

_____

I
$100 \div n = 10$

_____

Y
$n \div 4 = 3$

_____

L
$n \div 20 = 6$

_____

R
$7n = 14$

_____

D
$5n = 55$

_____

N
$n \div 12 = 12$

_____

T
$n \div 16 = 5$

_____

M
$10n = 130$

_____

R
$15n = 45$

_____

A
$2n = 28$

_____

C
$n \div 7 = 21$

_____

T
$4n = 60$

_____

___ ___ ___ ___ ___
13   14   2   10   16

___ ___ ___ ___
6   12   2   7

___ ___ ___ ___
120 14 144 11

___ ___ ___ ___ ___ ___ ___ ___ ___ ___
14 144 80 14   3 147 15 10 147 14

Name _____

PROBLEM SOLVING

HIGH FINANCE

Do this activity with a group. Imagine that you have $100 to divide among the members of the group. The only thing you must do is give each person a *different* sum of money. No two people can get the same amount. The arrangement you come up with must be agreed to by all the members of the group.

Here are some ideas:

- Give the most money to the oldest, the next amount to the next oldest, and so on.
- Give the money to the shortest, the next amount to the next shortest, and so on.
- Give each person $1 more than the next person.

1. Write down your own idea of how the money should be divided.

   _____

   _____

   _____

   _____

2. Now discuss ideas with your group. Set a time limit. At the end of the time, you must agree to an idea.

3. Write the group's decision here. Tell how much each person in the group gets.

   _____

   _____

   _____

   _____

4. Explain why you think the group agreed to this idea.

   _____

   _____

   _____

Name _____

COPYCAT

Try to copy each figure without lifting your pencil off the paper or going back over a line. The arrows in the first figure show one way that this figure can be drawn.

Some figures cannot be copied under these rules. Mark an X next to any figure that you can't copy.

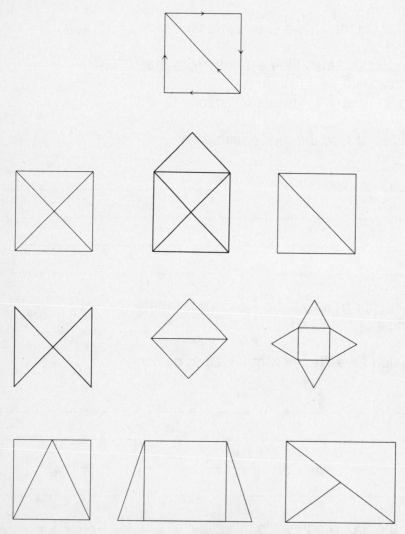

Can you think of a rule to explain which figures you can copy and which you can't? (Hint: Look at the number of lines that meet at each point in the figure. See how many are odd and how many are even.)

_____

_____

MACMILLAN/McGRAW-HILL

Name _____

ELAPSED TIME

On Your Own   Pair and Share   In a Group

SPECIAL AGENT

Work with a partner.

Imagine that you are travel agents. You are planning trips for these customers. Write the flights they should take and the total travel time, including layovers, of each trip. Use the schedule below.

Customer A wants to fly from Boston, Massachusetts, to Miami, Florida, on May 1. She wants to have some time in Miami to sightsee on the day she arrives. She returns to Boston on May 5.

To Miami: _____

To Boston: _____

Customer C wants to fly as late in the day as possible to Miami from Boston on April 30. She wants to return again as late as possible on May 2.

To Miami: _____

To Boston: _____

Customer C wants to fly as late in the day as possible to Miami from Boston on April 30. She wants to return again as late as possible on May 2.

To Miami: _____

To Boston: _____

SCHEDULE
All times are local.

NO.	FROM	TO	DEPART	ARRIVE
111	Boston	New York	9:00 A.M.	9:55 A.M.
126	Boston	New York	11:00 A.M.	11:55 A.M.
427	Boston	New York	3:00 P.M.	3:55 P.M.
512	New York	Boston	10:00 A.M.	10:55 A.M.
62	New York	Boston	2:00 P.M.	2:55 P.M.
109	New York	Boston	4:00 P.M.	4:55 P.M.
444	New York	Boston	7:00 P.M.	7:55 P.M.
156	New York	Miami	10:55 A.M.	1:25 P.M.
77	New York	Miami	6:00 P.M.	8:30 P.M.
621	Miami	New York	11:00 A.M.	1:30 P.M.
66	Miami	New York	3:00 P.M.	5:30 P.M.

MACMILLAN/McGRAW-HILL

MENTAL MATH: DIVIDING PATTERNS WITH POWERS OF 10

A SHRINKING VIOLET?

What gets shorter as it grows older?

Divide mentally. Then arrange the answers from least to greatest under the lines at the bottom of the page. Write the letter for each problem above it. You'll have to answer the riddle.

L
$78.2 \div 100$ _____

R
$3.2 \div 1,000$ _____

E
$14.33 \div 10$ _____

D
$67.44 \div 100$ _____

N
$0.078 \div 10$ _____

B
$0.113 \div 100$ _____

N
$122.3 \div 1,000$ _____

I
$34.6 \div 1,000$ _____

N
$566.1 \div 1,000$ _____

C
$1.8 \div 10$ _____

U
$2.03 \div 1,000$ _____

G
$14.92 \div 100$ _____

A
$45.1 \div 100$ _____

A
$0.3 \div 1,000$ _____

____

___ ___ ___ ___ ___ ___ ___ ___

___ ___ ___ ___ ___ ___

YOU CAN'T TELL THE PLAYERS WITHOUT A SCORECARD

Alan, Beth, Carrie, Debbie, and Elliot are on a basketball team.
They each live on a different street. The streets they live on are
1st, 2nd, 3rd, 4th, and 5th Streets.

Use the clues to match each player and his or her address. Put a
✔ for "yes" and an X for "no" in the chart below.

Clue 1	Alan lives two streets away from his cousin.
Clue 2	The team captain is not a boy.
Clue 3	Beth lives on the street next to Alan.
Clue 4	The team captain lives on 1st Street.
Clue 5	Debbie lives on the street next to the team captain.
Clue 6	Alan's cousin lives on 3rd Street.

Street

	1st	2nd	3rd	4th	5th
Alan					
Beth					
Carrie					
Debbie					
Elliot					

1. Alan lives on _____ Street.   2. Beth lives on _____ Street.

3. Carrie lives on _____ Street.   4. Debbie lives on _____ Street.

5. Elliot lives on _____ Street.

6. Who is the team captain? _____

7. Who is Alan's cousin? _____

MACMILLAN/McGRAW-HILL

Name

ZEROS IN THE QUOTIENT AND THE DIVIDEND

On Your Own   Pair and Share   In a Group

ZEROED OUT

Fill in the missing numbers in these division problems.

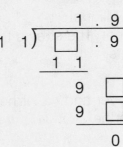

1.
```
        0 . 5 0 7
    3 ) 1 .  □  1
        1 5
          □    1
          □    1
               0
```

2.
```
           1 . 9
    1 1 )  □ . 9
           1 1
             9  □
             9  □
                0
```

3.
```
         0 . 1 1 □
    7 ) 0 . 8 □ □
         □
         1 □
           7
           3 □
           3 5
             0
```

4.
```
          2 . □ 6
    □ □ ) 2 4 . 7 2
          2 4
            7 □
            7 □
              0
```

5.
```
          0 . □ 3
    2 1 ) 2 . 1 □ 3
          2 1
            □ 3
            6 □
              0
```

6.
```
         1 . 1 □
    8 ) □ . 0 4
        8
        □ 0
          8
          2 4
          2 4
            0
```

7.
```
          □ . □ 1
    9 ) 8 □ . □ 9
        8 1
             9
           □
           0
```

8.
```
           0 . 1 □ 4
    3 3 ) 3 . □ 3 2
           3 3
             □ 3 2
             1 □
               0
```

9.
```
         1 . 5 □ 6
    4 ) □ . 3 □ 4
        4
        □ 3
        □ 0
          3 □
          □ 8
            2 4
            2 4
              0
```

MACMILLAN/McGRAW-HILL

Name _____

PROBLEM SOLVING

On Your Own   Pair and Share   In a Group

ARE THE ODDS EVEN?

Do this activity with a partner.

Make a set of number cards for the numbers 1 to 20. Use index cards or small paper squares.

Shuffle the cards and place them in a stack face down.

Player 1 takes two cards from the top of the stack and multiplies the numbers on them. If the product is an *odd* number, Player 1 keeps the cards and takes another turn. Player 1 continues until a product is even.

If the product is an even number, Player 1 puts the cards back anywhere in the stack. Player 2 takes a turn.

Example:

| 3 | 5 | $3 \times 5 = 15$ | **Player 1 keeps the cards and takes another turn** |

| 2 | 12 | $2 \times 12 = 24$ | **Player 1 puts the cards back.** |

Player 2 also draws two cards from the deck and multiplies the numbers. Player 2 keeps cards with *even* products and gets another turn. If the product is odd, Player 2 returns the cards to the stack.

1. Continue playing until all the cards are used up. Who won? _____

2. Reverse roles and play another game. Who won? _____

3. If possible, play another round of two games. Who won each time? _____

4. Is this game fair? Explain your answer.

_____

_____

_____

MACMILLAN/McGRAW-HILL

Name

DIVIDING DECIMALS BY DECIMALS

On Your Own   Pair and Share   In a Group

IF THE NUMBER FITS

For each problem, pick a divisor and quotient from the baskets to make a correct division problem. Use each number exactly once.

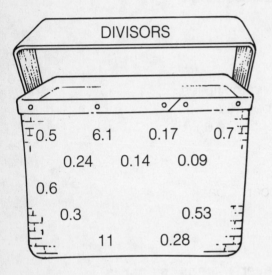

DIVISORS

0.5   6.1   0.17   0.7
0.24   0.14   0.09
0.6
0.3   0.53
11   0.28

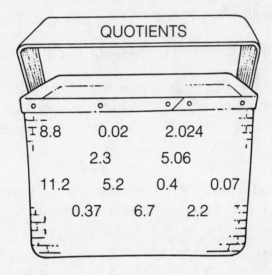

QUOTIENTS

8.8   0.02   2.024
2.3   5.06
11.2   5.2   0.4   0.07
0.37   6.7   2.2

1. 0.6072 ÷ _____ = _____

2. 1.608 ÷ _____ = _____

3. 5.6 ÷ _____ = _____

4. 1.232 ÷ _____ = _____

5. 3.542 ÷ _____ = _____

6. 1.166 ÷ _____ = _____

7. 0.391 ÷ _____ = _____

8. 0.468 ÷ _____ = _____

9. 0.427 ÷ _____ = _____

10. 0.1036 ÷ _____ = _____

11. 0.012 ÷ _____ = _____

12. 4.4 ÷ _____ = _____

SURPRISING SUMS

1. Write a two-digit number.   _____
    (The digits should not be the same.)

    Reverse the digits.   _____

    Subtract the smaller number from the larger.   _____

    Reverse the new number.   _____

    Add the last two numbers.   _____

Try this with other numbers. What answers do you get? Are they always the same?

_____

2. Write a two-digit number.   _____
    (The digits should not be the same.)

    Reverse it.   _____

    Subtract the smaller number.   _____

    Add the digits in the answer.   _____

Try this with other numbers. What answers do you get? Are they always the same?

_____

3. Write a number.   _____

    Double it.   _____

    Add 10.   _____

    Divide by 2.   _____

    Subtract the first number.   _____

Try this with other numbers. What answers do you get? Are they always the same?

_____

4. Write a number.   _____

    Add the next larger number.   _____

    Add 9.   _____

    Divide by 2.   _____

    Subtract the first number.   _____

Try this with other numbers. What answers do you get? Are they always the same?

_____

MACMILLAN/McGRAW-HILL

Name

ROUNDING DECIMAL QUOTIENTS

On Your Own   Pair and Share   In a Group

UNCOVER THE FACTS

What baseball player's record for the most home runs lasted from 1935 to 1974?

To find the facts, use your ruler to connect the problems on the left with the answers on the right. Round to the nearest place indicated in parentheses. Use your calculator.

2.5 ÷ 8	(tenth)	B	0.398
3.31 ÷ 7	(tenth)	Y A R	0.03
0.0976 ÷ 8	(hundredth)	O C	0.144
6.77 ÷ 17	(thousandth)	G B	0.847
0.25 ÷ 8	(hundredth)	E E	0.5
17.8 ÷ 5	(tenth)	B R	0.3
2.55 ÷ 5	(hundredth)	R U	0.4
89.3 ÷ 6	(thousandth)	L A M S	0.01
7.62 ÷ 9	(thousandth)	B V T	14.883
7.145 ÷ 18	(tenth)	N H E	3.6
4.887 ÷ 34	(thousandth)		0.51

Rearrange the letters that are not crossed out in the spaces below.

___ ___ ___ ___ ___ ___ ___ ___ ___

Now solve this problem to find out how many home runs the player hit. Round each division step to the nearest hundredth. Then round the answer to a whole number.

$$(8.273 ÷ 1.2) × (459.72 ÷ 9) × (16.98 ÷ 8.37) = \underline{\hspace{3cm}}$$

MACMILLAN/McGRAW-HILL

Name _____

ORDER OF OPERATIONS

On Your Own   Pair and Share   In a Group

FIGURE IT OUT

In the pattern below, there are two sets of figures. In each set, the figures are related in the same way: The second figure is a smaller version of the first.

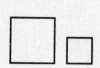 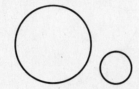

In each of the following patterns, ring the letter of the figure that completes the second set. The figures should be related in the same way in each set.

1.   **A**   **B**   **C**

2.   **A**   **B**   **C**

3.   **A**   **B**   **C**

4.   **A**   **B**   **C**

5.   **A**   **B**   **C**

6.   **A**   **B**   **C**

7.   **A**   **B**   **C**

MACMILLAN/McGRAW-HILL

Macmillan/McGraw-Hill, MATHEMATICS IN ACTION
Grade 6, Chapter 5, Lesson 10, pages 198–199

Name _____

On Your Own   Pair and Share   In a Group

STARRY SUMS

If you add the numbers on any of the lines through this
six-pointed star, you will get the sum 14.

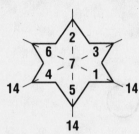

1. Use the numbers 8, 9, 10, 11, 12, 13, and 14.
   Place them in the star so the sums are 35.

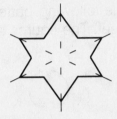

2. Use the numbers 1, 3, 5, 7, 9, 11, and 13.
   Place them in the star so the sums are 21.

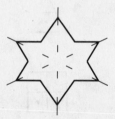

3. Use the numbers 1, 3, 5, 7, 9, 11, and 13 again.
   This time, the sums should be 25.

4. Now make up your own star so that all the sums equal 11.
   (Do not repeat any numbers.)

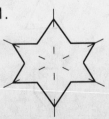

MACMILLAN/McGRAW-HILL

Name

CONVERTING METRIC MEASURES

On Your Own   Pair and Share   In a Group

WEIGH-IN TIME

Arrange these objects from lightest to heaviest. (You'll have to find a way to compare their masses first, since they are all given in different units.)

golf ball	45,900 mg
bowling ball	7,258 g
basketball	0.65 kg
softball	180 g
table tennis ball	240 cg
croquet ball	46.1 dg
baseball	1,559 dg
football	4.25 hg
volleyball	280,000 mg
soccer ball	45,400 cg
tennis ball	585 dg
squash ball	2,460 cg

Object   Mass

MACMILLAN/McGRAW-HILL

Name

PROBLEM SOLVING

On Your Own   Pair and Share   In a Group

TAKE IT IN STRIDE

Work with a partner on this activity.

One way to estimate a distance quickly is to "pace it off." A pace is the length of a step or a stride. If you know, for example, that you cover 2 feet in each step and that it takes you 6 steps to cross a room, then the room is about 6 × 2 or 12 feet wide.

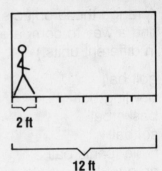

2 ft

12 ft

1. One partner will pace to estimate distances. First, find the length of that partner's step. Record the length of a step.

_____

2. Pick out some distances to measure in your classroom. List them in the first column below.

Distances to Measure	Estimates	Real Lengths

3. Now pace off each distance. Estimate the length. Record that measurement in the second column above.

4. Finally, measure each distance with a yardstick or measuring tape. Record the actual measurement in the third column above.

5. How well did you do in estimating?

_____

_____

6. How could you improve your estimating?

_____

_____

MACMILLAN/McGRAW-HILL

Name _____

MEAN, MEDIAN, MODE, AND RANGE

On Your Own   Pair and Share   In a Group

MAKE THE GRADE

Imagine that you are teacher for a day. Here are your students' scores on a math test. There are a possible 100 points on the test. What grade will you give each student?

In order to be fair, you should use some statistics to help you. You can calculate the mean, mode, median, and range of the scores. Make up a scale telling what scores get a passing grade (A, B, C, or D) and what scores fail (F).

Student	Score	Grade
1	81	
2	95	
3	86	
4	76	
5	81	
6	94	
7	73	
8	81	
9	100	
10	52	
11	79	
12	37	
13	86	
14	75	
15	93	
16	73	
17	76	
18	90	
19	87	
20	80	

Which type of statistic was most helpful in grading the test? _____

How many of each grade did you give?

A _____ B _____ C _____ D _____ F _____

What grade did you give to a test score that was the mean on the test? _____

What grade did you give to a test score that was the median on the test? _____

What grade did you give to a test score that was the mode on the test? _____

MACMILLAN/McGRAW-HILL

ENRICHMENT-59

Macmillan/McGraw-Hill, MATHEMATICS IN ACTION
Grade 6, Chapter 5, Lesson 14, pages 206–207

Name _____

EFFECTS OF CHANGES ON DATA

On Your Own   Pair and Share   In a Group

THE STATISTICS TOLD ME SO

For each set of statistics, write Y (for "yes") if you can draw the conclusion from the data given. Write N (for "no") if you cannot.

1. You are given the following data about the high temperatures (in °F) on each day in July 1989 and July 1990.

   The mean daily high in July 1989: 85°   in July 1990: 89.6°

   The median daily high in July 1989: 84°   in July 1990: 90°

   The range in July 1989: 26°   in July 1990: 18°

   The mode in July 1989: 77°   in July 1990: 84°

   a. _____ July 1990 had more days over 90° than July 1989.

   b. _____ The temperature did not reach 103° on any day in July 1990.

   c. _____ July 1989 was actually hotter than July 1990.

   d. _____ July 1990 had more hot days in a row than July 1989.

2. You are given the following data about the prices of eight items in a grocery store in January and October of the same year.

   The mean price in January: $1.62   in October: $1.72

   The median price in January: $1.22   in October: $1.32

   The range in January: $2.00   in October: $2.00

   The mode in January: $2.36   in October: $2.46

   a. _____ Between January and October, prices on the less expensive items remained the same, but prices on the more expensive items increased.

   b. _____ Prices on most items seem to have increased by $0.10.

   c. _____ The range of prices was much greater in October than in January.

   d. _____ Between January and October, about half the prices seem to have gone up, and about half seem to have gone down.

MACMILLAN/McGRAW-HILL

MENTAL MATH: DIVISIBILITY

On Your Own   Pair and Share   In a Group

MAYAN MATH

The Mayan Indians established a very advanced civilization
in Mexico almost 2,000 years ago. Here is how the numbers
0 through 19 were written in their number system.

0		10	← 2 fives
1		11	
2		12	
3		13	
4		14	
5		15	← 3 fives
6	← 5 plus 1	16	
7		17	
8		18	
9		19	

The Mayans used the idea of place value to build numbers. The
first place was the ones place. The next place was the twenties
place. Places were written vertically.

Second row: twenties place →
First row: ones place ⟶ } This number is 20: 1 twenty plus 0 ones.

Write the value of each of these Mayan numbers.

1. ·· _____

2. ⬭ _____

3. · _____

4. _____ _____

5. _____

6. ···· _____

7. ⬭ _____

8. _____ _____

Name

FACTORS AND GREATEST COMMON FACTOR

On Your Own   Pair and Share   In a Group

DAFFY DINO DEFINITION

Which dinosaur was the fastest?

Using a ruler, draw a line from the numbers on the left to their greatest common factor (GCF) on the right. The letters that remain will answer the question. Write the letters in order, reading from top to bottom, in the blank below.

1. 12, 28 •   P   • 15
          B
2. 40, 4, 2 •   R   • 4

3. 75, 25, 15 •   R   • 12
                                      O
4. 12, 24 •   O   • 20
                          N
5. 30, 40 •   N   • 16
                          T
6. 45, 60, 75 •   T   O   • 2

7. 60, 80 •   S   O   • 5

8. 16, 48, 80 • S   • 10
                                  A
9. 12, 18 •   A   U   • 8
                                          R
10. 14, 21 •   R   • 6

11. 45, 72, 90 •   U   S   • 9

12. 64, 24 •   U   S   • 7

The fastest dinosaur was the _____ .

MACMILLAN/McGRAW-HILL

PRIME AND COMPOSITE NUMBERS

On Your Own   Pair and Share   In a Group

AMAZING SIEVE

About 2,000 years ago, the Greek mathematician Eratosthenes devised a way to find prime numbers. His method is called the sieve of Eratosthenes. He took each number in succession (beginning with 2) and crossed out its multiples in a number table. The numbers that remained were prime. For example:

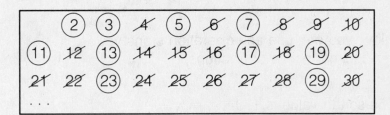

To tell if a number below 100 is prime, see if it can be divided by the first four prime numbers: 2, 3, 5, 7. If it *cannot*, it is prime.

In the number maze below, find the prime path from IN to OUT. Each number along the path must be a prime number, and your path must hit *all* the prime numbers. You may go across, down, up, or diagonally, but do not cross a number more than once. Use Eratosthenes' method to help you.

IN → 3	5	9	21	63
33	7	99	11	13
15	59	41	6	73
72	88	27	17	14
12	10	31	55	65
93	23	90	56	35
16	89	19	44	18
75	81	29	42	57
25	51	21	2	89

→ OUT

Macmillan/McGraw-Hill, MATHEMATICS IN ACTION
Grade 6, Chapter 6, Lesson 3, pages 230–231

MACMILLAN/McGRAW-HILL

Name

MULTIPLES AND LEAST COMMON MULTIPLE

On Your Own   Pair and Share   In a Group

CAREFUL ARRANGEMENTS

How can you arrange four 3s so the value is 36?
Here is one way:

(3 + 3) × (3 + 3)
6 × 6 = 36

In the puzzles below, you can use any operation signs you
choose, as well as decimal points or fractions.

1. Arrange four 5s so the value is 100.

_____

2. Arrange four 9s so the value is 153.

_____

3. Arrange four 9s so the value is 20.

_____

4. Arrange four 5s so the value is 2.5.

_____

5. Arrange four 3s so the value is 34.

_____

6. Arrange five 3s so the value is 17.

_____

7. Arrange five 2s so the value is 0.

_____

MACMILLAN/McGRAW-HILL

Name _____

PROBLEM SOLVING

AND THE NEXT NUMBER IS . . .

Work with a partner. Find the next two numbers in each pattern.
Then compare your answers with your partner's. Discuss any
differences in your answers.

1. 4 64 5 80 _____ _____

2. 5 10 15 5 20 _____ _____

3. 3 51 2 34 _____ _____

4. 8 20 44 92 _____ _____

5. 5 10 12 24 26 _____ _____

6. 13 9 10 6 7 3 _____ _____

7. 21 3 6 9 14 12 15 _____ _____

8. 19 10 90 81 729 _____ _____

9. 3 7 11 15 19 _____ _____

10. 6 11 7 12 8 _____ _____

11. 2 4 8 16 32 _____ _____

12. 35 3 70 6 105 9 _____ _____

13. 1,000 5 10 15 2,000 20 _____ _____

14. 7 10 9 12 11 14 _____ _____

15. 1 3 6 10 15 21 _____ _____

16. 5 25 20 4 9 45 40 8 _____ _____

Make up some patterns of your own. Give them to your partner
to solve.

17. _____ _____ _____ _____ _____ _____ ? ?

18. _____ _____ _____ _____ _____ _____ ? ?

19. _____ _____ _____ _____ _____ _____ ? ?

MACMILLAN/McGRAW-HILL

FRACTIONS AND EQUIVALENT FRACTIONS

On Your Own   Pair and Share   In a Group

FRACTURED FAIRY TALE

What fairy tale is about some talking vegetables?

Write an equivalent fraction for each of the following fractions.
Then find the answers under the lines below. Write the letter for
each fraction on the line. The first letter has been filled in.

H	A	A	K	L	T
$\frac{3}{8} = \frac{}{16}$	$\frac{4}{5} = \frac{}{10}$	$\frac{7}{8} = \frac{}{16}$	$\frac{6}{10} = \frac{}{5}$	$\frac{9}{10} = \frac{}{20}$	$\frac{1}{4} = \frac{}{16}$
A	E	A	K	N	D
$\frac{5}{10} = \frac{}{20}$	$\frac{3}{5} = \frac{}{10}$	$\frac{2}{4} = \frac{}{8}$	$\frac{8}{10} = \frac{}{5}$	$\frac{6}{8} = \frac{}{4}$	$\frac{10}{16} = \frac{}{8}$
B	C	S	T	N	E
$\frac{4}{10} = \frac{}{5}$	$\frac{6}{12} = \frac{}{4}$	$\frac{14}{20} = \frac{}{10}$	$\frac{3}{9} = \frac{}{3}$	$\frac{3}{6} = \frac{}{12}$	$\frac{1}{3} = \frac{}{6}$

$\underline{\text{J}}$ $\underline{\quad}$ $\underline{\quad}$ $\underline{\quad}$
$\quad$ $\frac{8}{10}$ $\frac{2}{4}$ $\frac{3}{5}$

$\underline{\quad}$ $\underline{\quad}$ $\underline{\quad}$
$\frac{14}{16}$ $\frac{3}{4}$ $\frac{5}{8}$

$\underline{\quad}$ $\underline{\quad}$ $\underline{\quad}$
$\frac{4}{16}$ $\frac{6}{16}$ $\frac{6}{10}$

$\underline{\quad}$ $\underline{\quad}$ $\underline{\quad}$ $\underline{\quad}$ $\underline{\quad}$
$\frac{2}{5}$ $\frac{2}{6}$ $\frac{4}{8}$ $\frac{6}{12}$ $\frac{7}{10}$

$\underline{\quad}$ $\underline{\quad}$ $\underline{\quad}$ $\underline{\quad}$
$\frac{1}{3}$ $\frac{10}{20}$ $\frac{18}{20}$ $\frac{4}{5}$

FRACTIONS IN SIMPLEST FORM

On Your Own   Pair and Share   In a Group

SIMPLER IS BETTER

Use these numerators and denominators to write problems
showing fractions and their simplest forms.

Numerators:

5	1	4	1	9	3	2	1	8	1	3	1
12	3	9	1	4	2	6	3	10	5	4	2

Denominators:

24	3	9	3	16	4	27	3	10	5	8	4
12	6	6	3	45	9	8	2	12	4	4	2

Use all the numbers in each group exactly once. Cross out
numbers as you use them. The first problem is done for you.

1. $\frac{4}{10} = \frac{2}{5}$ 2. — = —

3. — = —   4. — = —

5. — = —   6. — = —

7. — = —   8. — = —

9. — = —   10. — = —

11. — = —   12. — = —

MACMILLAN/McGRAW-HILL

Enrichment-67

Name _____

MIXED NUMBERS

CURIOUS CODE

In each problem, the numbers have been replaced by letters. Each letter always stands for the same number. It may be a 1-digit number or a 2-digit number. All answers are fractions or mixed numbers written in simplest terms.

Use the clue and logic to decide what number each letter stands for. Write the 12 letters and numbers on the lines below.

CLUE: L = 2

$$\frac{L}{F} = \frac{S}{L} \qquad\qquad \frac{A}{F} = S\frac{S}{F} \qquad\qquad \frac{E}{A} = S\frac{F}{A}$$

$$\frac{I}{E} = \frac{S}{I} \qquad\qquad \frac{O}{F} = L\frac{I}{F} \qquad\qquad \frac{H}{L} = I\frac{S}{L}$$

$$\frac{C}{F} = I \qquad\qquad \frac{T}{C} = \frac{S}{L} \qquad\qquad \frac{B}{T} = S\frac{S}{I}$$

$$\frac{Y}{F} = L\frac{S}{L}$$

Letter	Number	Letter	Number
L	2		

Now replace each number with its corresponding letter to get the answer to this riddle:

"How is a frog like a baseball player?"

___ ___ ___ ___ ___ ___ ___ ___ ___ ___ ___

___ ___ ___ ___ ___ ___

Name

COMPARING AND ORDERING

On Your Own   Pair and Share   In a Group

DAFFYNITIONS

To answer each riddle, write each group of fractions and mixed numbers in order from least to greatest. Write the letter of each number below the line.

What do you call the place where school lunches are made?

O	U	R	S	O	H	M	M
1	$\frac{2}{9}$	$\frac{2}{3}$	$\frac{1}{3}$	$\frac{7}{9}$	$\frac{4}{9}$	$\frac{1}{6}$	$1\frac{1}{3}$

___ ___ ___ ___ ___ ___ ___ ___

What do you call a twisted doughnut?

T	P	L	E	Z	E	R
$\frac{7}{12}$	$\frac{2}{12}$	$1\frac{1}{12}$	$\frac{1}{2}$	$\frac{3}{4}$	$\frac{11}{12}$	$\frac{1}{4}$

___ ___ ___ ___ ___ ___ ___

What do you call a cucumber in a sour mood?

I	L	K	P	C	E
$\frac{3}{16}$	$\frac{7}{16}$	$\frac{3}{8}$	$\frac{1}{8}$	$\frac{10}{32}$	$\frac{4}{8}$

___ ___ ___ ___ ___ ___

What do you call a song played on an automobile radio?

R	C	A	O	O	N	T
$1\frac{3}{8}$	$\frac{5}{8}$	$\frac{3}{4}$	$1\frac{3}{4}$	$1\frac{5}{8}$	$1\frac{11}{12}$	$1\frac{5}{12}$

___ ___ ___ ___ ___ ___ ___

MACMILLAN/McGRAW-HILL

Name _____

ROUNDING FRACTIONS AND MIXED NUMBERS

On Your Own   Pair and Share   In a Group

FRACTION ACTION

You can use mental math to decide if a fraction is greater than $\frac{1}{2}$.

Example: Is $\frac{3}{5} > \frac{1}{2}$?

Double the numerator. $2 \times 3 = 6$

If the result is greater than the denominator, $6 > 5$

the fraction is greater than $\frac{1}{2}$.   so $\frac{3}{5} > \frac{1}{2}$

Is the fraction greater than $\frac{1}{2}$? Write YES or NO.

1. $\frac{5}{9}$ _____ 2. $\frac{3}{7}$ _____ 3. $\frac{4}{11}$ _____ 4. $\frac{7}{15}$ _____

5. $\frac{7}{10}$ _____ 6. $\frac{8}{19}$ _____ 7. $\frac{13}{21}$ _____ 8. $\frac{11}{17}$ _____

In the maze below, find a path from START to END. Use only fractions that are greater than $\frac{1}{2}$. You may go up, down, across, or diagonally, but do not cross a number more than once.

$\frac{15}{16}$	$\frac{7}{15}$	$\frac{12}{30}$	$\frac{10}{24}$	$\frac{45}{90}$	END
$\frac{26}{50}$	$\frac{34}{70}$	$\frac{18}{32}$	$\frac{4}{7}$	$\frac{12}{25}$	$\frac{7}{11}$
$\frac{13}{20}$	$\frac{8}{15}$	$\frac{9}{20}$	$\frac{345}{700}$	$\frac{146}{300}$	$\frac{80}{150}$
$\frac{8}{14}$	$\frac{5}{12}$	$\frac{5}{13}$	$\frac{66}{130}$	$\frac{41}{81}$	$\frac{3}{7}$
$\frac{16}{33}$	$\frac{17}{33}$	$\frac{5}{10}$	$\frac{44}{87}$	$\frac{42}{90}$	$\frac{22}{44}$
START	$\frac{14}{28}$	$\frac{5}{9}$	$\frac{65}{130}$	$\frac{3}{5}$	$\frac{8}{18}$

MACMILLAN/McGRAW-HILL

Name

CUSTOMARY UNITS OF LENGTH

GOING TO GREAT LENGTH

Arrange these items from longest to shortest. (You'll have to find a way to compare their lengths first, since they are all given in different units.)

Remember, a mile is 5,280 feet.

White Sea–Baltic Canal, Soviet Union	141 mi
Golden Gate Bridge, California	1,400 yd
Simplon I Tunnel, Switzerland to Italy	12.3 mi
Sydney Harbor Bridge, Australia	19,800 in.
Panama Canal, Panama	50.7 mi
Mackinac Straits Bridge, Michigan	45,600 in.
Verrazano Narrows Bridge, New York	4,260 ft
Welland Canal, Canada	49,280 yd
Suez Canal, Egypt	100.6 mi
New River Gorge Bridge, West Virginia	1,700 ft
Rokko Tunnel, Japan	633,600 in.
Northern Line Subway Tunnel, England	30,488 yd

1. _____

2. _____

3. _____

4. _____

5. _____

6. _____

7. _____

8. _____

9. _____

10. _____

11. _____

12. _____

MACMILLAN/McGRAW-HILL

FIVE, SIX, PICK UP STICKS

To do these puzzles, you need 17 toothpicks or narrow strips of paper about as long as a toothpick.

1. Arrange your toothpicks so they form this pattern.

Now move just 3 of the toothpicks and make 5 squares, all the same size. Draw the new figure you made here.

2. Make this pattern.

Move just 4 of the toothpicks to make 3 squares. Draw the new figure you made.

3. Make this pattern.

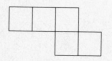

Move just 2 of the toothpicks to make 4 squares. Draw the new figure you made.

4. Make this pattern. Take away 6 toothpicks to spell a word number—without moving the remaining toothpicks.

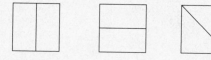

Draw the new figure.

MACMILLAN/McGRAW-HILL

FRACTIONS, MIXED NUMBERS, AND DECIMALS

On Your Own   Pair and Share   In a Group

CROSSHATCH

Try to find a decimal in columns 3 and 4 that matches each fraction or mixed number in columns 1 and 2. When you find a match, cross out both the numbers and the letters next to them. A match may be found in any row. An example is done for you.

COLUMN 1	COLUMN 2	COLUMN 3	COLUMN 4
C $1\frac{1}{10}$ (crossed out)	A $\frac{5}{10}$	U 0.34	A 0.5
E $\frac{75}{1,000}$	P $4\frac{89}{100}$	E 6.25	T 0.11
O $\frac{1}{4}$	E $\frac{3}{4}$	B 0.25	D 1.1
T $\frac{3}{8}$	I $7\frac{99}{100}$	E 0.75	A 4.089
B $2\frac{5}{1,000}$	R $6\frac{1}{8}$	Q 9.855	E 2.005
T $\frac{6}{10}$	I $1\frac{1}{4}$	N 6.125	E 9.12
N $\frac{12}{10}$	N $9\frac{1}{2}$	A 7.099	S 7.5
E $\frac{4}{10}$	O $\frac{32}{1,000}$	M 0.4	T 1.25
H $3\frac{2}{100}$	T $\frac{7}{10}$	L 1.02	L 2.8

Now write the letters that are left in each column on the line.
Unscramble each group of letters to spell a familiar mathematical word.

COLUMN 1 _____   _____

COLUMN 2 _____   _____

COLUMN 3 _____   _____

COLUMN 4 _____   _____

MACMILLAN/McGRAW-HILL

PROBLEM SOLVING

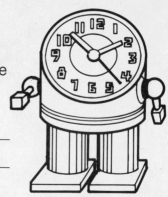

On Your Own   Pair and Share   In a Group

IT'S ABOUT TIME

Work with a group to discuss and solve these problems.

1. The clock on the bookshelf is 5 minutes fast. The clock on the cabinet has stopped at 8:00. Which clock is correct more times during the day? Why?

   _____

   _____

2. A clock shows the correct time at midnight. That clock then loses exactly 30 minutes a day every day after that. In how many days will that clock show the correct time again?

   _____

3. Suppose the clock loses 1 hour a day. When will it show the correct time?

   _____

4. A timer beeps every 3 minutes. Another beeps every 8 minutes. A third beeps every 12 minutes. From 1:00 to 2:00, when do any two of these timers beep together? When do all

   three beep together?_____

5. How many seconds in a minute? An hour? A day?

   _____

6. A millisecond is 0.001 seconds. How many milliseconds in a

   second? In a minute?_____

7. A nanosecond is 0.000000001 seconds. How many

   nanoseconds in a second? In a millisecond?_____

8. Which is longer, 600,000 milliseconds or 12 minutes?

   _____

MACMILLAN/McGRAW-HILL

Name _____

ESTIMATING SUMS AND DIFFERENCES

On Your Own   Pair and Share   In a Group

BULL'S-EYE

Estimate the sum or difference of the number in the center of each bull's-eye and each of the numbers in the first ring. Round to the nearest whole number to estimate. Write the estimate in the outer ring. What do you notice about the outer rings?

1. Add.

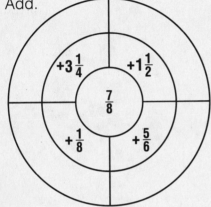

2. Subtract.

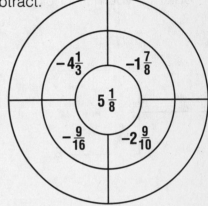

3. Add.

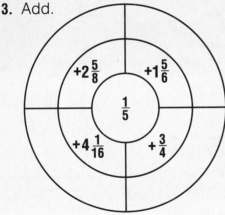

4. Subtract.

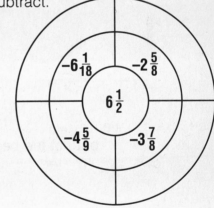

5. Work with a partner.
Try making up some addition or subtraction rings of your own.
The outer ring should fit the pattern you found above.
Trade papers with some friends. Solve each other's puzzles.

MACMILLAN/McGRAW-HILL

FLOWER ARRANGEMENTS

Here are two drawings showing four flowers and a bee. The four flowers are exactly the same length.

In each drawing, can you move only two flowers so that you make the next pattern? Circle the flowers you would move and draw an arrow to show where you would put them. (Use pencils to model each problem if you need help.)

1.

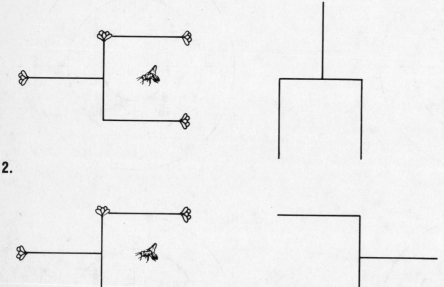

2.

Can you make a pattern where the bee is not inside the flowers? Move just two flowers, but not the bee. Draw the new pattern. Show which flowers you moved.

3.

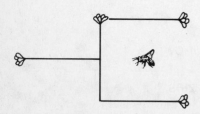

MACMILLAN/McGRAW-HILL

Name

ADDING FRACTIONS: UNLIKE DENOMINATORS

On Your Own   Pair and Share   In a Group

THE MISSING LINK

Fill in the boxes with the missing numbers. Each fraction in these problems should be in its simplest form.

1.
$$\frac{1}{2}$$
$$+\frac{\Box}{\Box}$$
$$\overline{\quad}$$
$$\frac{3}{4}$$

2.
$$\frac{\Box}{6}$$
$$+\frac{\Box}{3}$$
$$\overline{\quad}$$
$$\frac{1}{2}$$

3.
$$\frac{3}{8}$$
$$\frac{1}{\Box}$$
$$\overline{\quad}$$
$$\frac{5}{8}$$

4.
$$\frac{5}{\Box}$$
$$+\frac{3}{\Box}$$
$$\overline{\quad}$$
$$\frac{1}{2}$$

5.
$$\frac{1}{3}$$
$$+\frac{\Box}{4}$$
$$\overline{\quad}$$
$$\frac{7}{12}$$

6.
$$\frac{1}{3}$$
$$+\frac{\Box}{6}$$
$$\overline{\quad}$$
$$1\frac{1}{\Box}$$

7.
$$\frac{\Box}{10}$$
$$+\frac{9}{10}$$
$$\overline{\quad}$$
$$1\frac{1}{\Box}$$

8.
$$\frac{\Box}{4}$$
$$+\frac{\Box}{8}$$
$$\overline{\quad}$$
$$\Box\frac{3}{\Box}$$

MACMILLAN/McGRAW-HILL

Macmillan/McGraw-Hill, MATHEMATICS IN ACTION
Grade 6, Chapter 7, Lesson 3, pages 278–279

Name _____

SUBTRACTING FRACTIONS: UNLIKE DENOMINATORS

On Your Own   Pair and Share   In a Group

PICK A PAIR

1. Which two numbers have a sum of exactly $\frac{1}{2}$?

$$\boxed{\quad \frac{1}{3} \qquad \frac{1}{4} \qquad \frac{1}{3} \qquad \frac{1}{4} \qquad \frac{1}{8} \qquad \frac{1}{8} \quad}$$

_____

2. Which two numbers have a difference of $\frac{1}{8}$?

$$\boxed{\quad \frac{5}{8} \qquad \frac{1}{3} \qquad \frac{3}{8} \qquad \frac{9}{16} \qquad \frac{3}{16} \qquad \frac{1}{4} \quad}$$

_____

3. Which two numbers have the sum that is closest to 1?

$$\boxed{\quad \frac{9}{10} \qquad \frac{3}{8} \qquad \frac{1}{20} \qquad \frac{9}{16} \qquad \frac{1}{5} \quad}$$

_____

4. Which two numbers have the difference that is closest to $\frac{1}{2}$?

$$\boxed{\quad \frac{7}{10} \qquad \frac{3}{4} \qquad \frac{1}{8} \qquad \frac{9}{16} \qquad \frac{1}{12} \quad}$$

_____

MACMILLAN/McGRAW-HILL

Name _____

PROBLEM SOLVING

ALL ABOARD!

Work with a partner on this activity.

Imagine that you are scheduling trains from Smithville to Metro City.

- There are two trains assigned to this route—Train A and Train B. Each one can carry 1,500 people.
- Both trains make the trip from Smithville to Metro City or back in 1 h and 10 min. Each time a train reaches either city, it needs 20 min to refuel before it returns.
- Between 6:00 A.M. and 8:30 A.M., 1,400 people an hour want to leave Smithville for Metro City. An average of 700 people an hour want to go from Metro City to Smithville.
- Between 4:00 P.M. and 6:30 p.m., 1,400 people an hour want to return to Smithville. An average of 850 people an hour want to go from Smithville to Metro City.
- During the rest of the day, an average of 500 people an hour want to ride in either direction. Trains do not depart after 9:01 P.M.

1. Complete the schedules. Show each train that will run from Smithville to Metro City and from Metro City to Smithville.

2. The railroad needs fares from an average of 750 people to run a train in either direction. (Extra money that is collected on one trip can be used to pay for trains running at other times.) Will the railroad make money, "break even," or lose money on the schedule you have prepared?

_____

3. What could the railroad do to improve its profits? _____

_____

Smithville to Metro City			
Leave	Arrive	Train	No. of Riders
6:00 A.M.	7:10 A.M.	A	1,400
7:30		B	

Metro City to Smithville			
Leave	Arrive	Train	No. of Riders
6:00 A.M.	7:10 A.M.	B	700

MACMILLAN/McGRAW-HILL

Name _____

ADDING MIXED NUMBERS

On Your Own   Pair and Share   In a Group

WHAT'S FOR DINNER?

What's the best kind of pie to take on a picnic?

Write the answer to each problem. Then find each answer at the bottom. Write the letter for each problem on the line to answer the riddle.

P $3\frac{1}{5}$
    $+2\frac{3}{5}$

O $4\frac{1}{6}$
    $+3\frac{1}{12}$

H $12\frac{1}{3}$
    $+\ 3\frac{2}{9}$

F $1\frac{3}{8}$
    $+1\frac{1}{4}$

Y $4\frac{2}{9}$
    $+1\frac{1}{3}$

S $9\frac{1}{5}$
    $+1\frac{3}{5}$

I $1\frac{11}{12}$
    $+4\frac{1}{4}$

E $1\frac{1}{6}$
    $+1\frac{1}{8}$

L $3\frac{1}{4}+2\frac{1}{4}+6\frac{1}{2}$

O $7\frac{9}{10}+1\frac{1}{5}+2\frac{1}{2}$

$10\frac{4}{5}$ ___ $15\frac{5}{9}$ ___ $11\frac{3}{5}$ ___ $7\frac{1}{4}$ ___

$2\frac{5}{8}$ ___ 12 ___ $5\frac{5}{9}$ ___

$5\frac{4}{5}$ ___ $6\frac{1}{6}$ ___ $2\frac{7}{24}$ ___

MACMILLAN/McGRAW-HILL

PART MAGIC

Fill in the missing fractions in each magic square. The sum should
be the same across, down, and on the diagonals of each square.

1.

$\frac{1}{12}$	$\frac{1}{6}$	$\frac{1}{4}$
$\frac{1}{12}$		

Magic Sum _____

2.

$\frac{3}{4}$		
0		
$\frac{3}{4}$		$\frac{1}{4}$

Magic Sum _____

3.

$\frac{4}{5}$		
	1	
$1\frac{3}{5}$		$1\frac{1}{5}$

Magic Sum _____

MATH WIZARD

Here's a math trick that you can use to show your friends what a genius you are. But first see if you can figure out how the trick works.

In this trick, you multiply any nine-digit number by another nine-digit number.

Start with any nine-digit number: **812,335,672** for example.

Always multiply by 142,857,143.

$$\begin{array}{r} \mathbf{812{,}335{,}672} \\ \times\,\mathbf{142{,}857{,}143} \\ \hline \end{array}$$

To get the answer, you actually divide. Imagine that the first nine-digit number is repeated. Divide it by 7.

$$\begin{array}{r} \mathbf{116{,}047{,}953{,}258{,}905{,}096} \\ 7\,\overline{)\,\mathbf{812{,}335{,}672{,}812{,}335{,}672}} \end{array}$$

repeated

So, 812,335,672 × 142,857,143 is 116,047,953,258,905,096.

1. Now try this trick with 156,782,345.

$$\begin{array}{r} 156{,}782{,}345 \\ \times\,142{,}857{,}143 \\ \hline \end{array}$$

2. Try another number: show your work.

3. The trick works because the number you always multiply by is $\frac{1}{7}$ of 1 billion and 1. What happens when you multiply a nine-digit number by 1 billion and 1? Try it and see.

_____

4. Now, since 142,857,143 is $\frac{1}{7}$ of 1 billion and 1, what do you divide by?

_____

MACMILLAN/McGRAW-HILL

PROBLEM SOLVING

On Your Own   Pair and Share   In a Group

YOU BE THE TEACHER

Imagine that you are a teacher and that the problems below were solved by some of your students. Look at each problem. If the answer is correct, place a ✔ next to it. If the answer is incorrect, give the correct solution. Then explain the error so you can help your students do better work. The first one is done for you.

1. Student A

```
   856
   723
 + 624
 2,193  2,203
```
Error: _Did not regroup correctly._

2. Student B

$145.56 + 236.3 + 99.732 = 1,166.47$

Error: _____

_____

3. Student C

A box of paper plates costs $1.79 and a box of cups costs $.79. How much change do you receive from $20 if you buy 6 boxes of plates and 5 boxes of cups?

Error: _____ $5.31 _____

_____

4. Student D

A dozen pencils costs $2.79 and a dozen pens costs $5.95. How much more do 3 dozen pens cost than 2 dozen pencils?

Error: _____ $23.43 _____

_____

5. Student E

A box can hold 15 books. How many boxes will you need to pack 110 books?

Error: _____ 7 boxes _____

_____

_____

6. Student F

$6 \times (15 + 4) - 2 = 92$

Error: _____

_____

_____

MULTIPLYING FRACTIONS

FLIPPER AND FRIENDS

What kind of animal is a dolphin or porpoise?

Match the multiplication problem on the left to the answer on the right. Write the letter of the answer in the box. The letters will spell the answer to the question.

1. ☐ $\frac{1}{4} \times \frac{2}{3}$ W 1

2. ☐ $\frac{3}{5} \times \frac{1}{3}$ A $\frac{7}{10}$

3. ☐ $\frac{7}{8} \times \frac{4}{5}$ A 4

4. ☐ $3 \times \frac{2}{3}$ S $\frac{1}{6}$

5. ☐ $\frac{3}{9} \times \frac{1}{4}$ H $\frac{1}{8}$

6. ☐ $4 \times \frac{1}{4}$ L $\frac{1}{12}$

7. ☐ $\frac{5}{16} \times \frac{2}{5}$ E $\frac{21}{40}$

8. ☐ $6 \times \frac{2}{3}$ L 2

9. ☐ $\frac{4}{5} \times \frac{3}{4}$ M $\frac{1}{5}$

10. ☐ $\frac{7}{10} \times \frac{3}{4}$ L $\frac{3}{5}$

Name _____

YOU'RE THE BOSS

Work with a group of friends. Imagine that you are the student council and you are in charge of the school supplies store. It is your responsibility to make the work schedule. These are the jobs.

> Two clerks for before school hours 7:45 A.M. to 8:15 A.M.
> Two clerks for lunchtime hours 12:00 to 12:30 P.M.
> Two clerks for lunchtime hours 12:30 P.M. to 1:00 P.M.
> Two clerks for after school hours 2:30 P.M. to 3:00 P.M.

Here are the students who will work in the store. Students either eat lunch from 12:00 to 12:30 P.M. or from 12:30 P.M. to 1:00 P.M. Most students can get to school by 7:45 A.M. if necessary.

1. Abby usually arrives at school at 8:15 A.M. Lunch at 12:00.

2. Keisha usually arrives at school at 8:15 A.M. Lunch at 12:30 P.M. Band practice 11:30 A.M. to 12:30 P.M. Mon., Wed., and Fri.

3. William has lunch at 12:30 P.M.

4. Noah has to leave every day at 2:30 P.M. Lunch at 12:00.

5. Darla usually arrives at school at 8:00 A.M. Lunch at 12:30 P.M. Has clubs after school on Tuesday and Thursday.

6. Patrice usually arrives at school at 8:15 A.M. Lunch at 12:00. Has choir practice at 12:30 P.M. on Monday and Wednesday. Leaves at 2:30 P.M. every day.

7. Suellen has lunch at 12:00.

8. Joel usually arrives at school at 8:15 A.M. Has lunch at 12:30 P.M.

Confer with your group. Make up a work schedule. Try to give every student the same number of hours.

	M	T	W	TH	F
7:45–8:15					
12:00–12:30					
12:30–1:00					
2:30–3:00					

MACMILLAN/McGRAW-HILL

Name _____

MULTIPLYING FRACTIONS AND MIXED NUMBERS

On Your Own   Pair and Share   In a Group

ALL MIXED UP

Each series of fractions and mixed numbers follows a rule. Check the next number for each series. Each number should be in lowest terms.

1. $1\frac{1}{8}$, $1\frac{1}{4}$, $1\frac{3}{8}$, ? | $1\frac{1}{2}$ $1\frac{2}{8}$ $\frac{1}{2}$

2. $\frac{7}{16}$, $\frac{9}{16}$, $\frac{1}{2}$, $\frac{5}{8}$, ? | $\frac{7}{16}$ $\frac{9}{16}$ $1\frac{1}{8}$

3. $1\frac{1}{5}$, $1\frac{8}{15}$, $1\frac{11}{15}$, $2\frac{1}{15}$, ? | $2\frac{3}{15}$ $2\frac{2}{5}$ $2\frac{4}{15}$

4. $2\frac{1}{9}$, $2\frac{7}{9}$, $2\frac{2}{3}$, $3\frac{1}{3}$, ? | 3 $3\frac{1}{9}$ $3\frac{2}{9}$

5. $6\frac{1}{4}$, $6\frac{1}{12}$, $6\frac{5}{12}$, $6\frac{1}{4}$, ? | $6\frac{7}{12}$ $6\frac{3}{4}$ $6\frac{11}{12}$

6. $\frac{3}{10}$, $1\frac{1}{2}$, $1\frac{1}{4}$, $2\frac{9}{20}$, ? | 2 $2\frac{4}{20}$ $2\frac{1}{5}$

7. $1\frac{1}{8}$, $2\frac{1}{4}$, $3\frac{3}{8}$, $4\frac{1}{2}$, ? | $5\frac{5}{8}$ $5\frac{1}{2}$ $5\frac{1}{4}$

Name _____

MULTIPLYING MIXED NUMBERS

On Your Own   Pair and Share   In a Group

POSITIVELY PYRAMIDS

What numbers do cooks like?

Multiply the number at the top of each triangle by the numbers in the circles in the second row. Write the answers in simplest form in the bottom circles. Then arrange the answers in order from least to greatest on the lines below. Copy the letter from each answer.

Numbers in order: ___ ___ ___ ___ ___ ___ ___ ___ ___ ___ ___ ___

Letters: ___ ___ ___ ___ ___ ___ ___ ___ ___ ___ ___ ___

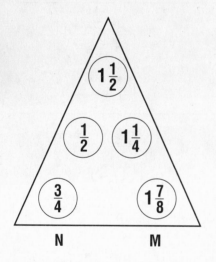

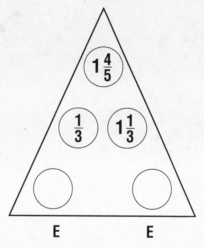

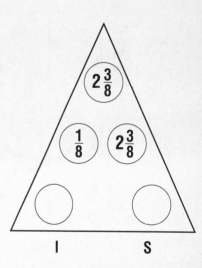

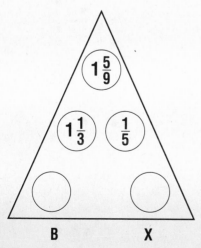

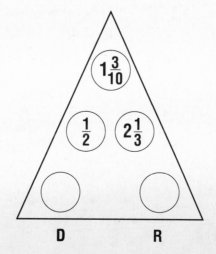

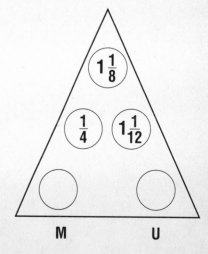

Name

PROBLEM SOLVING

On Your Own   Pair and Share   In a Group

UPSIDE DOWN AND SIDEWAYS

Work with a partner.

Look at the first number cube in each row. Then find one other figure in the row that *could be* another view of the same number cube. You and your partner should both agree on each answer.

Circle your choice.

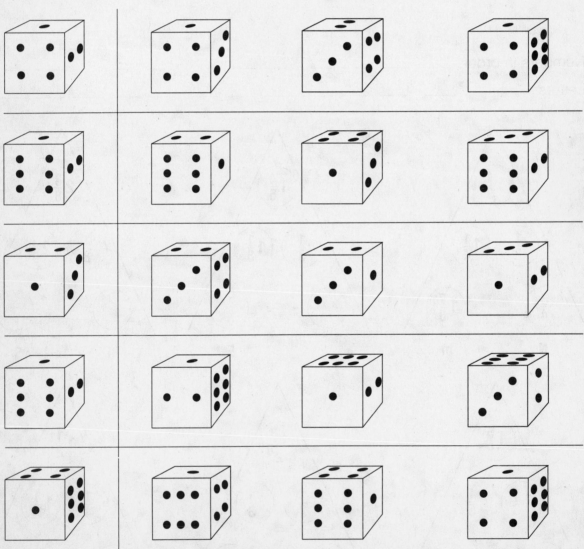

MACMILLAN/McGRAW-HILL

Name _____

DIVIDING FRACTIONS: COMMON DENOMINATORS

On Your Own   Pair and Share   In a Group

ALL BOXED IN

Write division problems. Pick a dividend from Box 1. Pick a divisor from Box 2. Pick a quotient from Box 3. Use each number only once.

Problems: _____

_____

_____

_____

_____

_____

_____

_____

Box 1

$\frac{3}{5}$	$\frac{7}{9}$	$\frac{11}{20}$	$\frac{4}{7}$	$\frac{7}{10}$	$\frac{5}{8}$	$\frac{17}{20}$	$\frac{5}{9}$
$\frac{9}{10}$	$\frac{6}{7}$	$\frac{6}{7}$	$\frac{3}{8}$	$\frac{2}{3}$	$\frac{9}{20}$	$\frac{4}{5}$	

Box 2

$\frac{5}{20}$	$\frac{5}{20}$	$\frac{1}{9}$	$\frac{1}{5}$	$\frac{4}{8}$	$\frac{4}{20}$	$\frac{1}{7}$	$\frac{1}{3}$
$\frac{2}{7}$	$\frac{2}{8}$	$\frac{2}{9}$	$\frac{2}{5}$	$\frac{2}{10}$	$\frac{3}{10}$	$\frac{2}{7}$	

Box 3

3	2	7	3	$1\frac{1}{2}$	$2\frac{1}{3}$	2	$4\frac{1}{2}$
$1\frac{1}{4}$	$2\frac{3}{4}$	$3\frac{2}{5}$	6	2	$1\frac{4}{5}$	$2\frac{1}{2}$	

How many problems did you write? _____

Score: 12–15   You're a math whiz!
         8–11   OK, Einstein did as well!
         <8   Come on! You can do better than that!

MACMILLAN/McGRAW-HILL

Macmillan/McGraw-Hill, MATHEMATICS IN ACTION
Grade 6, Chapter 8, Lesson 9, pages 328–329

Name

GO WITH THE FLOW

Work with a partner on the activities below.
You can show a series of steps with a flowchart.
Write each step in a box. Use these shapes.

⬭ Beginning or end ◇ For a yes/no question ▭ For instructions

Here's an example of a flowchart for crossing the street:

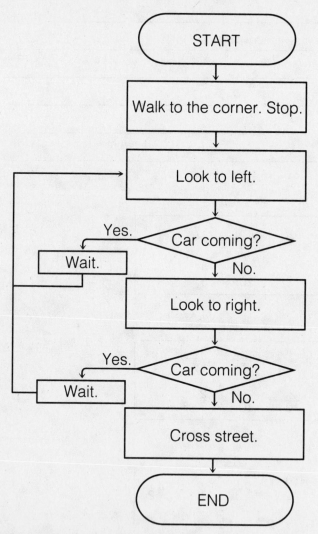

Pick one of these situations or make up your own.

Adding two fractions	Making a phone call
Dividing two fractions	Buying a pair of shoes
Multiplying two fractions	Brushing your teeth

Draw flowchart. Use the back of the page.

MACMILLAN/McGRAW-HILL

PROBLEM SOLVING

BACK TO THE FUTURE

Do this activity with a group. Divide the group into pairs that compete against one another. Each pair should solve the problems. The first pair to answer all the questions correctly wins.

1. Anne is three times as old as Brad. In 5 years the sum of their ages will be 30. How old is each of them today?

_____

2. Jerome has a collection of football cards. Jason has twice as many as Jerome. Bethanne has half as many as Jerome and Jason combined. Sarah has 115 fewer cards than Bethanne. Sarah has 110 cards. How many cards does Jerome have?

_____

3. A football team scores a total of 330 points in 10 games. In each game, the team scores 6 more points than the game before. After what game does that team's *total* score reach 90 points?

_____

4. Together, Michael and Jennifer have saved money for 5 months. Each month, Jennifer has saved twice as much as the month before. Each month, Michael has saved half as much as Jennifer. The total saved at the end of 5 months is $139.50. How much has each of them saved?

_____

5. There were 100 marbles in a bag. Piero's friend took some out. Piero counted and found he had 34 left. How many did his friend take?

_____

6. Marva and Sherry each took 12 sheets of paper. There were 45 sheets of paper left in the stack. How many sheets of paper were there to begin with?

_____

7. Joseph went to the store with $10.00 He bought groceries and came home with $4.30. How much did the groceries cost?

_____

Macmillan/McGraw-Hill, MATHEMATICS IN ACTION
Grade 6, Chapter 8, Lesson 11, pages 332–333

Name _____

CONVERTING CUSTOMARY MEASURES

On Your Own   Pair and Share   In a Group

MIXED-UP MEASUREMENTS

Find the spot on this map where the treasure is buried. Follow the directions, drawing the path described. The line for the first measurement is given.

1. right 1 ft
2. down $\frac{1}{2}$ yd
3. left 6 in.
4. down $1\frac{1}{2}$ ft
5. right $\frac{1}{3}$ yd
6. down 2 yd
7. right $\frac{1}{1,760}$ mi

8. up $\frac{2}{3}$ yd
9. right $\frac{2}{5,280}$ mi
10. up $\frac{6}{12}$ ft
11. right $\frac{1}{6}$ yd
12. up $\frac{5}{6}$ yd
13. right $\frac{1}{2}$ of $\frac{1}{5,280}$ mi
14. up $\frac{3}{4}$ yd

The treasure is at _____

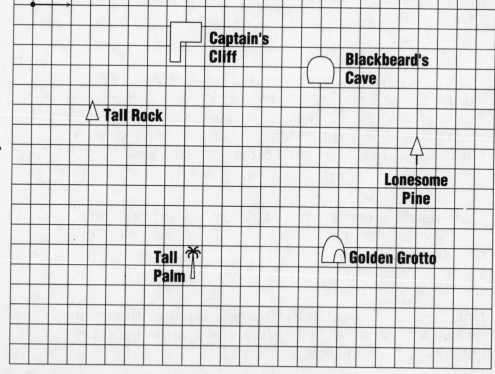

Scale:
1 square = 6 in.

MACMILLAN/McGRAW-HILL

Name _____

AREAS OF PARALLELOGRAMS AND TRIANGLES

On Your Own   Pair and Share   In a Group

AREA RUGS

At Cheap Charlie's Carpet Emporium, there are some rugs with unusual shapes. Charlie charges $1.00 a square foot for any rug. Figure out the total area of each rug. Write the price on the price tag.

1.
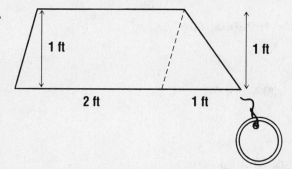

1 ft   1 ft
2 ft   1 ft

2.

5 ft
4 ft   1 ft   1 ft

3.

6 ft
3 ft
2 ft

4.

2 ft   2 ft
2 ft

5.
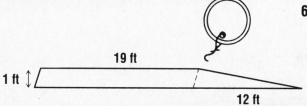

19 ft
1 ft
12 ft

6.
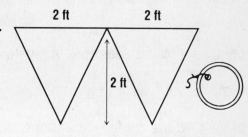

3 ft   3 ft
3 ft   4 ft
2 ft

7.
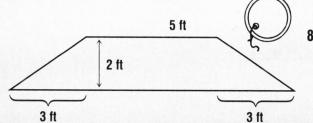

5 ft
2 ft
3 ft   3 ft

8.
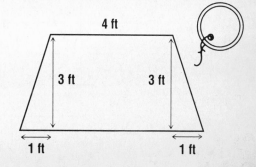

4 ft
3 ft   3 ft
1 ft   1 ft

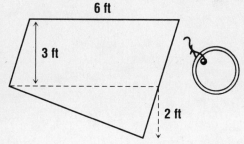
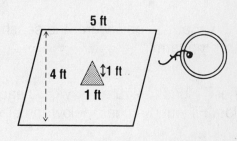
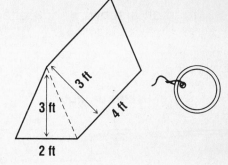

MACMILLAN/McGRAW-HILL

Name

WHO'S WHO

Angela, Brad, Cheryl, Daniella, and Ethan each went on a
vacation trip. Each went to a different place. None went to the
same place he or she went to last year.

The five vacation spots were: the seashore, the mountains, a lake,
a city, and a farm.

Use these clues to figure out where each person went on
vacation. Fill out the chart below to help you.

- The person who went to a farm last year went to a lake this
  year.

- Angela went to the seashore last year.

- One of the boys went to a farm.

- Brad went to the same place that Daniella went last year.

- Ethan rode on a subway and visited tall buildings on his
  vacation.

	Seashore	Mountains	Lake	City	Farm
Angela					
Brad					
Cheryl					
Daniella					
Ethan					

MACMILLAN/McGRAW-HILL

Name _____

MEASURING ANGLES

On Your Own   Pair and Share   In a Group

FINDING ALL THE ANGLES

Isn't this a logical idea? Suppose the numerals we use were shaped as follows: each numeral contained as many angles as the number it represented. For example, the numeral for "one" might be written this way so that it contained exactly one angle:

one angle

For each numeral below, number the angles. Show that each numeral contains the correct number of angles:

1.

2.

3.

4.

5.

6.

7.

8.

9. Can you figure out how the numeral for "nine" should be written?

MACMILLAN/McGRAW-HILL

Macmillan/McGraw-Hill, MATHEMATICS IN ACTION
Grade 6, Chapter 9, Lesson 2, pages 356–357

Name _____

PERPENDICULAR AND PARALLEL LINES

PAIR PATTERNS

Work with a partner.

The two pairs of figures are related in the same way. In the first pair, the first figure has three sides; the second has one more. In the second pair, the second figure again has one more side than the first.

  |

Find the relationship between the first pair of figures. Draw the figure that completes the second pair. Then make up some pair patterns of your own. Try them out on a friend.

1. |

2. |

3. |

4. |

5. |

MACMILLAN/McGRAW-HILL

Name _____

COMPASS CONSTRUCTIONS

On Your Own   Pair and Share   In a Group

PERFECT MATCHES

What did the team call its young, impolite pitcher?

The two columns below list the angles and line segments of this symmetrical figure. Draw a line from each angle or line segment on the left to the congruent angle or line segment on the right. The lines will cross through some of the letters. Write the remaining letters at the bottom in the order they appear.

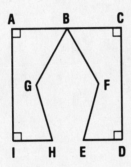

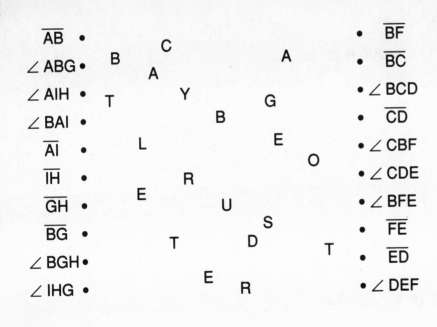

$\overline{AB}$ •

∠ ABG •

∠ AIH •

∠ BAI •

$\overline{AI}$ •

$\overline{IH}$ •

$\overline{GH}$ •

$\overline{BG}$ •

∠ BGH •

∠ IHG •

• $\overline{BF}$

• $\overline{BC}$

• ∠ BCD

• $\overline{CD}$

• ∠ CBF

• ∠ CDE

• ∠ BFE

• $\overline{FE}$

• $\overline{ED}$

• ∠ DEF

___ ___ ___ ___   ___ ___ ___ ___

MACMILLAN/McGRAW-HILL

Name _____

TRIANGLES

THREE SIDES TO THE QUESTION

There is a pattern to some right triangles. If you know the lengths of two of the sides, you can tell the length of the third side without measuring.

On a separate piece of paper, draw each of the following triangles. (Use an inch or centimeter ruler to measure the third side.)

1. Draw a right triangle with these measurements.

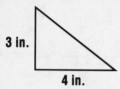

3 in.

4 in.

Measure the length of the third side. _____

2. Draw this right triangle. The third side is _____ .

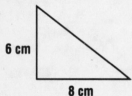

6 cm

8 cm

3. Draw this right triangle. The third side is _____ .

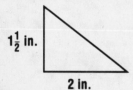

$1\frac{1}{2}$ in.

2 in.

4. What pattern have you found?

_____

_____

What is the third side of each of the following triangles? (Don't draw or measure.)

5. Right triangle *ABC* has sides of 3 cm and 4 cm.

   The longest side is _____ .

6. Right triangle *DEF* has sides of 9 ft and 12 ft.

   The longest side is _____ .

7. Right triangle *GHI* has sides of 4.5 cm and 6 cm.

   The longest side is _____ .

MACMILLAN/McGRAW-HILL

Name

QUADRILATERALS

CUTUPS

1. There are several ways to cut a rectangle into four congruent rectangles. Draw lines to show two ways to cut the rectangles.

2. Draw lines to show how to divide this triangle into four congruent triangles.

3. Draw lines to show how to divide this triangle into nine congruent triangles.

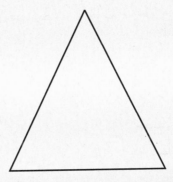

OTHER POLYGONS

On Your Own   Pair and Share   In a Group

COMBOS

There are three shapes on the left. Which of the figures on the right can be formed from the three shapes? The shapes can be moved or turned in any direction, but not flipped.

1. Figures: _____

a.

b.

c.

d.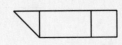

2. Figures: _____

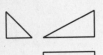

a.

b.

c.

d.

3. Figures: _____

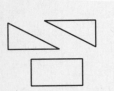

a.

b.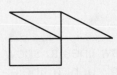

c.

d.

4. Figures: _____

a.

b.

c.

d.

Name _____

PROBLEM SOLVING

On Your Own   Pair and Share   In a Group

NUMBERS IN DISGUISE

Work with a partner.

A. Each of the letters in these problems stands for a number from
0 to 9. Can you break the code and see which letter stands
for which number?

1.
```
  E
+ D
----
  E
```

2.
```
  A
+ B
----
 HD
```

3.
```
  C
+ C
----
 HD
```

4.
```
  C
+ H
----
  G
```

5.
```
  G
+ J
----
 HD
```

6.
```
 HH
+ GG
----
 II
```

7.
```
  I
+ G
----
 HE
```

8.
```
  F
- E
----
  G
```

9.
```
  F
+ A
----
 HH
```

CODE

A = _____

B = _____

C = _____

D = _____

E = _____

F = _____

G = _____

H = _____

I = _____

J = _____

B. Try making up your own set of coded problems. Check your
work carefully. Exchange papers with another group and solve
each other's problems.

MACMILLAN/McGRAW-HILL

CONGRUENCE AND SIMILARITY

On Your Own   Pair and Share   In a Group

SEEING IS BELIEVING

1. Find three triangles that are the same size and shape.

2. Find two flags that have the same size poles and are pointing the same way.

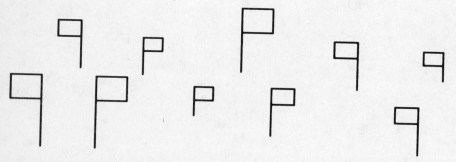

3. Find two that are the same and in the same position.

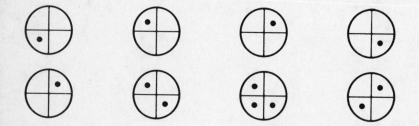

4. Find two pairs that are the same shape but not the same size.

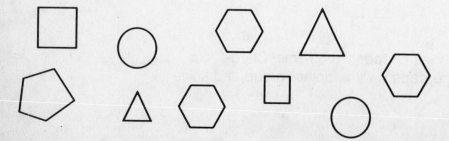

MACMILLAN/McGRAW-HILL

ENRICHMENT-103

SYMMETRY AND REFLECTIONS

On Your Own   Pair and Share   In a Group

SIMPLY SYMMETRICAL

Work with a partner.

A. Which of these letter patterns are symmetrical? Put a check
mark by each symmetrical pattern.

1.   A
     ↔
     A

2. A ↕ A

3. MOM ↕ MOM

4.   MOM
     ↔
     WOW

5.   WOW
     ↔
     WOW

6. TEAR ↕ ЯAET

7.   BOB
     ↔
     BOB

8. TRAM ↕ TЯAM

B. Write the reflection of each word. (You can check your
answers in a mirror to see if you are correct.)

9. WHAM ↕

10. TOP ↔

11. MIRROR ↔

12. BOX ↕

C. Experiment with other words. Can you and your partner find
other symmetrical words? Try writing just the reflection of a
word and ask another friend to figure out the word.

MACMILLAN/McGRAW-HILL

Enrichment-103

Macmillan/McGraw-Hill, MATHEMATICS IN ACTION
Grade 6, Chapter 9, Lesson 11, pages 374–375

TRANSLATIONS AND ROTATIONS

On Your Own   Pair and Share   In a Group

SLIDES AND TURNS

This figure was translated 2 squares to the right and then rotated a half turn.

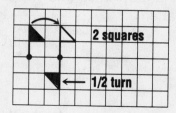

For each figure, draw the figure after it is translated and rotated.

1. Translate 3 squares right and rotate a half turn.

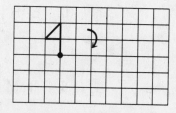

2. Translate 2 squares right and 1 down. Rotate a half turn.

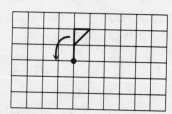

3. Translate 1 square left and 1 down. Rotate a quarter turn.

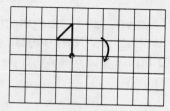

4. Translate 1 square right and 1 down. Rotate a three-quarter turn.

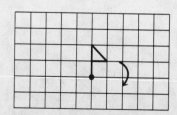

MACMILLAN/McGRAW-HILL

PROBLEM SOLVING

On Your Own   Pair and Share   In a Group

QUIZ SHOW

Work with a group to run a quiz show. Pick two people to be the contestants. Let the other members of the group make up five problems that can be solved with the strategies listed below. Examples are given for the first two strategies.

1. Strategy—Make a List

   Example: Bob has 3 different pairs of pants and 3 T-shirts.
   How many different outfits can he wear? (9)

   Your problem: _____

   _____

2. Strategy—Look for a Pattern
   Example: What is the missing number in the sequence

   3, 6, 10, __, 21, 28? (15)

   Your problem: _____

   _____

3. Strategy—Solve a Multistep Program
   Your problem: _____

   _____

   _____

4. Strategy—Work Backward
   Your problem: _____

   _____

   _____

5. Write and Solve a Number Sentence
   Your problem: _____

   _____

   _____

Now pick one person to read the problems, one at a time, to the contestants. The first contestant to solve each problem gets a point. The contestant with the most points wins.

MACMILLAN/McGRAW-HILL

Name

RATIOS AND RATES

ME AND MY SHADOW

Here are some patterns where shadows are seen on a sidewalk
square. Estimate the ratio of light area to shadow in each square.
Write the ratio.

1.
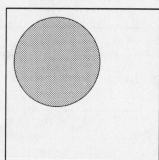

2.
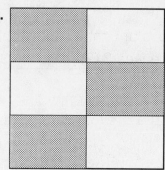

3.
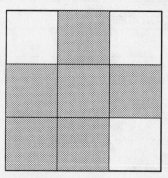

4.
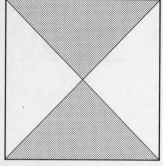

5.
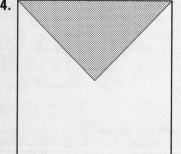

6.
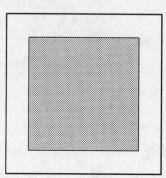

7.
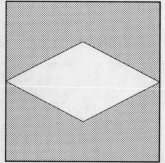

8.
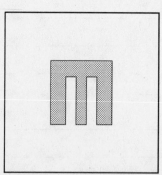

9.
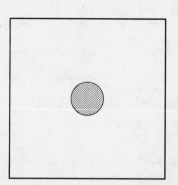

EQUAL RATIOS

On Your Own   Pair and Share   In a Group

BARGAIN HUNTING

At Sly Sal's Supermarket, you have to be careful. Sometimes what looks like a bargain isn't really a bargain. Look at each of these signs. Decide if you get a bargain by buying the larger quantity.

Write B if it is a bargain to buy the larger quantity. Write N if it is not.

1.

TOMATOES

$1.00 a pound
$3.00 for 4 pounds

2.

PINEAPPLES

75¢ for 1
$2.30 for 3

3.

EGGS

$1.05 a dozen
$3.90 for 4 dozen

4.

SPONGES

35¢ for 2
$3.50 for 10

5.

ROLLS

$1.26 a dozen rolls
$5.40 for 48 rolls

6.

MILK

65¢ for 1 quart
$2.50 for 1 gallon

7.

HAMBURGER MEAT

$3.50 for 2 pounds
$9.25 for 5 pounds

8.

APPLES

22¢ for 1
$1.50 for 8

9. Work with a group of friends. Visit a supermarket (or use advertisements) and make notes about prices for different sizes or quantities of various items (for example, breakfast cereal, canned vegetables, orange juice). Decide which prices are bargains and which are not. Make up a set of problems based on what you find. Trade problems with another group.

MACMILLAN/McGRAW-HILL

Name

PROPORTIONS

On Your Own   Pair and Share   In a Group

PUZZLING PATTERN

About how many volcanoes are there in the world?

To find out, solve each proportion. Write the answer. Then color in the space at the bottom with that number in it. The pattern you make will tell you the answer. Don't let your eyes trick you before you solve the problems.

1. $\frac{1}{8} = \frac{n}{16}$

2. $\frac{3}{5} = \frac{6}{n}$

3. $\frac{12}{n} = \frac{1}{3}$

4. $\frac{n}{27} = \frac{6}{18}$

5. $\frac{10}{100} = \frac{5}{n}$

6. $\frac{48}{n} = \frac{2}{4}$

7. $\frac{2.3}{4.6} = \frac{n}{6.2}$

8. $\frac{7}{49} = \frac{12}{n}$

9. $\frac{30}{12} = \frac{n}{40}$

10. $\frac{66}{n} = \frac{22}{2}$

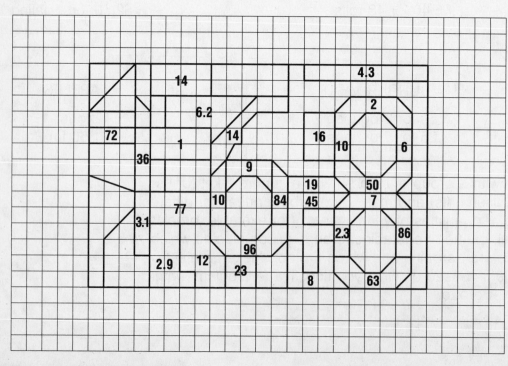

Name _____

SCALE DRAWINGS

On Your Own   Pair and Share   In a Group

WANT TO BUY A BRIDGE?

Here's an easy way to copy a picture and make it larger or smaller.
Copy this picture of the Brooklyn Bridge. Make it twice as large.

Step 1. Draw a grid across the drawing of the bridge on this page. Make your grid squares $\frac{1}{2}$ inch across.

Step 2. Draw a grid in the rectangle at the bottom. Make the squares 1 inch across.

Step 3. Copy what is in each square of the small picture into the same square of the larger picture.

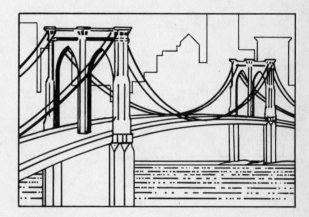

MACMILLAN/McGRAW-HILL

Macmillan/McGraw-Hill, MATHEMATICS IN ACTION
Grade 6, Chapter 10, Lesson 4, pages 402–403

On Your Own   Pair and Share   In a Group

X MARKS THE SPOT

Topographic maps are special kinds of maps that show elevation.
The *contour lines* on the map are drawn through points of the
same elevation above sea level. For example, here, the line that is
marked goes through a point 100 ft above sea level. A line is
drawn for every 10 feet above or below that. So point X is at an
elevation of 80 feet.

Interval = 10 feet

Look at this map to answer the questions below.

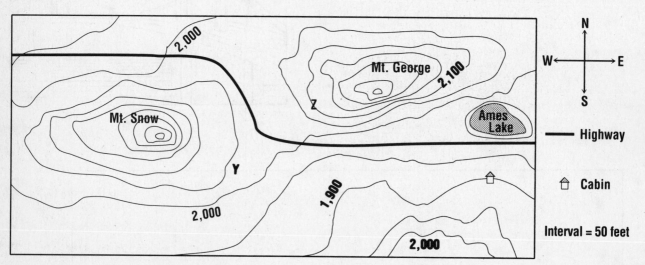

1. What is the elevation of point Y? _____

2. What is the elevation of point Z? _____

3. Which mountain is higher, Mt. Snow or Mt. George? _____

4. What is the elevation of the cabin? _____

5. What is the elevation of the shore of Ames Lake? _____

6. Which side of Mt. George is steepest? _____

MACMILLAN/McGRAW-HILL

Name _____

PROBLEM SOLVING

On Your Own   Pair and Share   In a Group

FIT THE PROBLEM TO THE ANSWER

Work with a partner to write a problem that can be solved by
each number sentence. Use the facts given in each problem.
Add missing facts if you need to. Then solve each problem.
Here is an example.

**Maria buys a scarf.
She pays with a $20 bill.
Change = $14.05
Number sentence: $20 − n = $14.05
Problem: How much did the scarf cost?
Answer: $5.95**

Now write and solve the problems below.

1. Three books are on a shelf.
Total number of pages = 678

Number sentence: $156 + 168 + n = 678$

Problem: _____

Answer: _____

_____

_____

2. Andrew sells tickets.
Total price of tickets sold = $25

Number Sentence: $n \times \$2.50 = \$25$

Problem: _____

Answer: _____

_____

_____

3. Samantha makes shirts.
Each shirt takes 2.5 yd of fabric.

Number Sentence: $15 \div n = 2.5$

Problem: _____

Answer: _____

_____

_____

MACMILLAN/McGRAW-HILL

Macmillan/McGraw-Hill, MATHEMATICS IN ACTION
Grade 6, Chapter 10, Lesson 6, pages 406–407

Name _____

PERCENTS AND DECIMALS

On Your Own   Pair and Share   In a Group

ANIMAL DOCTOR

What do you call a sick crocodile?

Write each answer. Then find and cross out the answer in one of the boxes at the bottom. When you are finished, the remaining letters, written in order, will give you the answer to the question.

Write the percent as a decimal.

1. 50% _____   2. 102% _____   3. 9% _____   4. 27% _____

5. 0.4% _____   6. 18% _____   7. 20% _____   8. 4.1% _____

Write the decimal as a percent.

9. 0.02 _____   10. 1.4 _____   11. 1.04 _____   12. 0.6 _____

13. 0.007 _____   14. 2 _____   15. 0.81 _____

I	I	L	L	O	L
0.05	0.5	50	0.09	0.18	2.7
I	L	O	I	G	G
27.0	0.27	0.2	1.02	10.20	0.004
A	E	A	T	T	C
0.04	0.041	2%	20%	140%	81%
L	O	O	R	O	S
200%	104%	780%	78%	60%	0.7%

A sick crocodile is an ___ ___ ___ ___ ___ ___.

PERCENTS AND FRACTIONS

On Your Own   Pair and Share   In a Group

BATTER UP

Work with some friends. Pretend you are the new statisticians for your school's baseball team. Figure out each of the following stats. These definitions should help. Discuss them with your group to be sure you understand them.

> **Earned-run average (ERA):** A decimal figured by dividing a pitcher's earned runs by the total innings pitched and then multiplying by 9. Express ERAs to the nearest hundredth. **Example:** 2.50

> **Batting average:** A decimal figured by dividing a player's total number of hits by the total times at bat. (Batting averages do not have zeros in front of the decimal points.) Express batting averages to the nearest thousandth. **Example:** .296

> **Wins:** A decimal figured from the fraction of wins over total games played. Win percentages are written like batting averages.

> **Fielding average:** A decimal figured by dividing a fielder's total outs and assists by the total chances a fielder has. Fielding averages are written like batting averages.

1. Sammy got a hit 9 out of 27 times at bat. What is his batting

    average? _____

2. Brad had 45 chances to field the ball this season. He got 20 outs and 10 assists.

    What is his fielding average? _____

3. Shawanda pitched 5 innings; 2 runs were earned against her.

    What is her ERA for the game? _____

4. Shawanda pitched 24 innings in all this season. A total of 10 runs were earned against her.

    What is her ERA for the season? _____

5. The team played 20 games this year and won 11 of them.

    What is the team's win percentage? _____

6. Now work with your group to create some baseball statistic problems of your own. Trade work with another group and solve each other's problems.

MACMILLAN/McGRAW-HILL

PROBLEM SOLVING

On Your Own   Pair and Share   In a Group

CIRCULAR REASONING

Work with a partner to interpret these circle graphs. Discuss each question and write your answer.

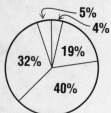

"Land Use in the Philippines
Total area: about 116,000 mi²"
Sections: 32% farmland, 5% irrigated farmland,
4% pasture, 40% forest, 19% other

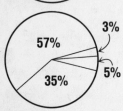

"Land Use in Canada
Total area: about 3,550,000 mi²"
Sections: 5% farmland, 3% pasture, 35% forest,
57% other

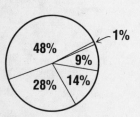

"Land Use in the United Kingdom (England,
Scotland, Wales, Northern Ireland)
Total area: about 94,000 mi²"
Sections: 28% farmland, 1% irrigated farmland,
48% pasture, 9% forest, 14% other

1. Which country is the largest?
_____

2. Which country is the smallest?
_____

3. Which country is probably the driest? Why?
_____
_____

4. Which country probably raises the most cattle or sheep? Why?
_____
_____

5. What kinds of land use might the word "other" refer to?
_____
_____

6. Can you tell which country has the largest cities and the greatest number of city dwellers? Why or why not?
_____
_____

7. Which country has the smallest number of acres of farmland?
_____
_____

8. Can you tell which country has the most trees? Why or why not?
_____
_____

MACMILLAN/McGRAW-HILL

Name _____

CIRCLES AND CIRCUMFERENCE

On Your Own   Pair and Share   In a Group

DOING WHEELIES

You know that you can measure the distance between two points with a ruler or yardstick.

You can also use a circular object to measure. The object can be a bicycle wheel, the rim of a cup, or any other object in the shape of a circle.

Make a mark at any point on the circle. Put that mark at the point where you want to start measuring.

distance to measure

Roll your circle along. Count each full turn of the circle.

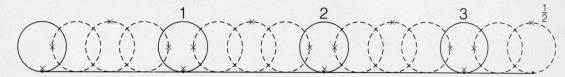

When you get to the end point, estimate what fraction of the circle was used in the last turn.

Now, use a string or tape measure to find the circumference of the circle. Multiply the circumference times the number of turns you made. This is the distance the circle traveled.

$$3\frac{1}{2} \times 1\frac{1}{2} \text{ in.} = 5\frac{1}{4} \text{ in.}$$

circumference = $1\frac{1}{2}$ in.

Work with a partner. Pick a circular object. (It can be a toothpaste cap, a bracelet, a cup, and so on.) Pick a distance to measure. (It can be a desk top, a book, and so on.)

Complete.

1. Object used to measure: _____ Object measured: _____

   Number of turns: _____ Circumference: _____ Distance: _____

2. Use a different object.

   Number of turns: _____ Circumference: _____ Distance: _____

3. When might you use this kind of measurement? Discuss with your partner.

_____

_____

MACMILLAN/McGRAW-HILL

Name _____

FINDING CIRCUMFERENCE

On Your Own   Pair and Share   In a Group

THE LONG WAY AROUND

What is the distance around each figure? Round your answers to the nearest tenth.

1.

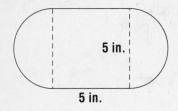

5 in.

5 in.

_____

2.

20 cm

_____

3.

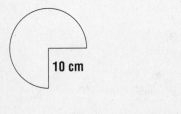

10 cm

_____

4.

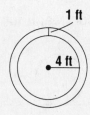

1 ft

4 ft

_____
(distance around
outer circle)

5.

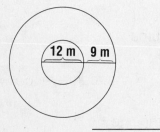

12 m   9 m

_____
(distance around
outer circle)

6.

4 in.   4 in.

4 in.

_____

7.

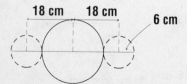

18 cm   18 cm   6 cm

_____
(distance around
all three circles)

8.

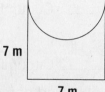

7 m

7 m

_____

MACMILLAN/McGRAW-HILL

Name

AREA OF A CIRCLE

On Your Own Pair and Share In a Group

CIRCULAR REASONING

What kind of circle does a truck driver like?

Find the area of each circle. Use a calculator to help you. Then find each answer on the wheel at the bottom. Write the letter for each answer on the wheel. Read around the circle to answer the question.

1. C 10 m _____

2. E 6 m _____

3. R 8 m _____

4. L 4.6 m _____

5. I 4 m _____

6. E 5 m _____

7. S 9 m _____

8. C 3.9 m _____

9. I 6.2 m _____

10. M 24 m _____

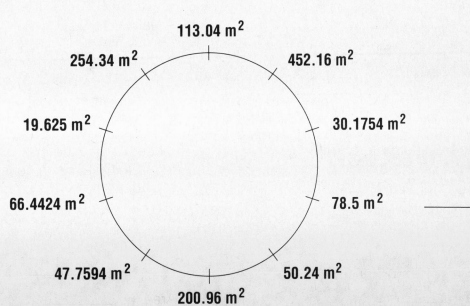

113.04 m²
254.34 m²
452.16 m²
19.625 m²
30.1754 m²
66.4424 m²
78.5 m² _____
47.7594 m²
50.24 m²
200.96 m²

MACMILLAN/McGRAW-HILL

Macmillan/McGraw-Hill, MATHEMATICS IN ACTION
Grade 6, Chapter 11, Lesson 3, pages 440–441

AREAS OF IRREGULAR FIGURES

On Your Own   Pair and Share   In a Group

FIGURE THIS

Each of these problems can be solved in two ways. Work with a partner to find both solutions. Your answers should be the same in each case.

1. Find the area of this triangle.
a. Use the formula Area $= \frac{1}{2}$ base × height.

Area = _____

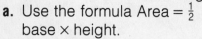
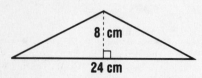

b. Draw a diagram showing how you could cut the triangle into two pieces to make a rectangle. Give the dimensions of the rectangle and find its area.

Area = _____

2. Find the area of this figure.
a. Use a formula for each part.

Area = _____

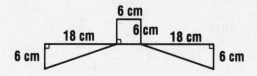

b. Show how you can rearrange the pieces to find the area with one formula. Give the dimensions of your diagram.

Area = _____

3. Find the area of this figure.
a. Use a formula for each part.

Area = _____

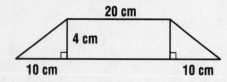

b. Show how you could rearrange the pieces to find the area with one formula. Give the dimensions of your diagram.

Area = _____

4. Find the area of this figure.
a. Use a formula for each part.

Area = _____

b. Show how you could rearrange the pieces to find the area with one formula. Give the dimensions of your diagram.

Area = _____

AREAS OF COMPOUND FIGURES

On Your Own   Pair and Share   In a Group

CLEVER CUTTING

Work with a partner to figure out this puzzle. Can you cut the
figure below into 4 pieces (A, B, C, D) that will fit together and
form a perfect square? You may cut only along the horizontal or
vertical lines. First, draw lines within the figure to show how you
would cut the pieces. Trace or copy the figure several times to
experiment with your choices. When you find the solution, draw a
diagram of it below. Show how your 4 pieces make a square.

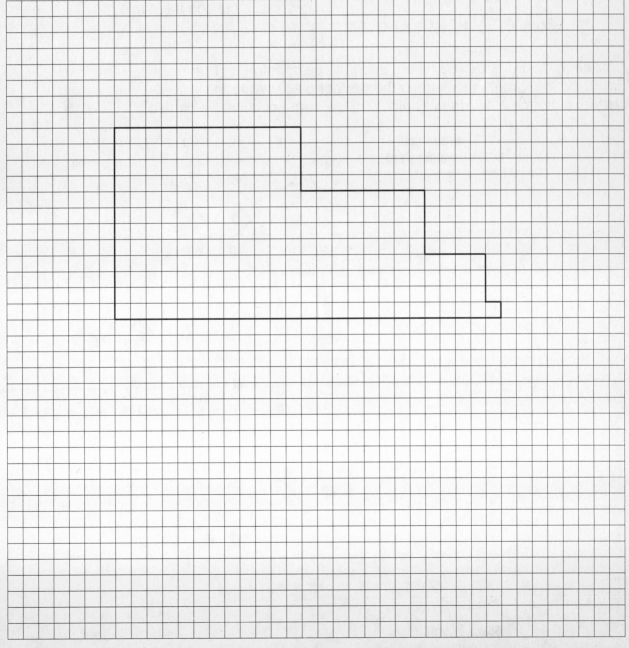

MACMILLAN/McGRAW-HILL

PROBLEM SOLVING

On Your Own   Pair and Share   In a Group

THINGS IN COMMON

In this diagram, the shapes in the left circle all have something in common. They are all shaded. The shapes in the right circle all have four or more straight sides. In the middle, where the circles overlap, are the shapes which fit into both groups—they are shaded with four or more straight sides.

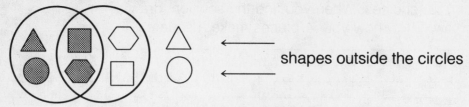

shapes outside the circles

For each diagram, decide where each shape should go. Then write the *letter* of each shape in the correct place. Write the letters of shapes that do not belong in any circle outside the circles.

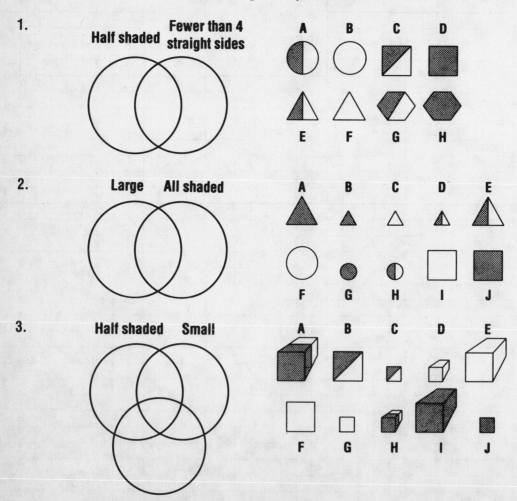

1.

Half shaded   Fewer than 4 straight sides

A   B   C   D

E   F   G   H

2.

Large   All shaded

A   B   C   D   E

F   G   H   I   J

3.

Half shaded   Small

A   B   C   D   E

F   G   H   I   J

Space figure

Name _____

DRAWING SPACE FIGURES

On Your Own   Pair and Share   In a Group

KEEPING IT IN PERSPECTIVE

A. When you draw space figures, give a feeling of depth. Draw in **perspective.** As you look at a real object, like railroad tracks, for example, parallel lines *seem* to get closer in the distance. When you draw, instead of drawing lines parallel, make them get closer in the distance too.

Here are some rules:

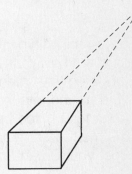

- Use parallel lines for any surface facing you, like the front of this prism.

- Make lines of surfaces that are receding (going away) from you slant towards each other slightly, like the top of this prism.

- Use the same slant for lines that go in the same direction.

Complete these figures. Use perspective.

1. Rectangular prism

2. Triangular prism

3. Rectangular prism

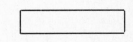

B. Artists pick a point on their page and call it the vanishing point. All the receding parallel lines would meet at that point if they were extended far enough.

4. Draw a house. Pick a vanishing point. All receding parallel lines should meet at that point. Use the back of this page.

vanishing point

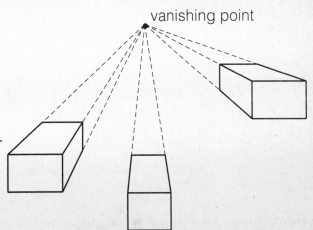

ENRICHMENT-122

Name _____

VOLUME OF TRIANGULAR PRISM

On Your Own   Pair and Share   In a Group

A PINCH OF SALT

Many doctors suggest that Americans consume less sodium for healthier living. Sodium is the mineral found in table salt. One diet recommends a moderate level of up to 3,300 milligrams of sodium a day. Work with a group to find out what foods you could eat to stay within the 3,300 mg limit.

• Record a day's menu that includes foods a student in your group might typically eat in a day.
• Find out how many milligrams of sodium are in each of the foods on your menu.
• Add up the total sodium content.
• If the total is too high (more than 3,300 mg), make changes in the menu to cut the sodium content down.
• Post your Smart Sodium menu in your classroom.

This list of the sodium content of foods will help you. You can find more information on sodium on the labels of all packaged foods.

	Sodium Content		Sodium Content
White bread, 1 slice	117 mg	Peanut butter, 2 tbsp	167 mg
Corn flakes, 1 oz	320 mg	Fast-food hamburger	1,000 mg
Tomato soup, 1 c	1,050 mg	Ketchup, 1 tbsp	154 mg
Milk, 1 c	130 mg	Chocolate shake, 12 oz	329 mg
American cheese, 1 oz	238 mg	Canned green beans, 1 c	925 mg

Typical Day's Menu

Breakfast	Food	Mg of Sodium	Dinner	Food	Mg of Sodium
	_____	_____		_____	_____
	_____	_____		_____	_____
	_____	_____		_____	_____
	_____	_____		_____	_____
Lunch	_____	_____	Snacks	_____	_____
	_____	_____		_____	_____
	_____	_____		_____	_____
				_____	_____

Total: _____

Remember: Always eat a balanced diet. Too little sodium can be unhealthful too!

MACMILLAN/McGRAW-HILL

VOLUME OF A CYLINDER

CYLINDER SLICE-UPS

Part of each of these space figures has been cut out. Find the volume of the remainder.

Assume that when you see a shape cut out of one face of a figure, that cut goes through the entire figure. So, if you see a circle cut out of one side, the cutout figure is a cylinder.

1.

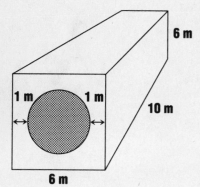

3.

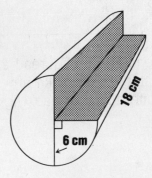

2.

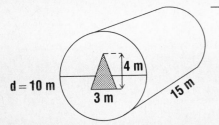

4.

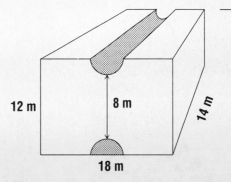

MACMILLAN/McGRAW-HILL

Name

PROBLEM SOLVING

On Your Own   Pair and Share   In a Group

CUTOUTS

Work with a partner to make models of space figures from paper or cardboard. Here is an example of a pattern for a rectangular prism. The pattern is made to be drawn on cardboard, cut on the solid lines, and folded on the dotted lines. The tabs are to be hooked into the slots.

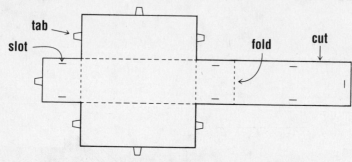

tab

slot

fold

cut

Create a pattern for each of the figures below. Try out each pattern to be sure that it works. Make any necessary corrections and draw the final pattern next to each figure.

1.

2.
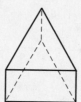

3.

4.

MACMILLAN/McGRAW-HILL

PROBABILITY

On Your Own   Pair and Share   In a Group

MIX AND MATCH

A. There are 10 white socks and 10 black socks in a drawer. Sachi reaches into the drawer without looking.

1. What is the probability that he will pick a white sock?

_____

2. What is the probability that he will pick a black sock?

_____

3. Sachi picks a white sock. Now he needs a match. What is the probability that he will pick a white sock from the drawer on the next try?

_____

4. Sachi picks a black sock. Now he has 1 white sock and 1 black sock. What is the probability that he will have a pair of matching socks on the next try?

_____

5. Suppose the light is out so that Sachi can't see the colors of the socks he picks. How many socks should he pick from the original 20 to be sure of getting at least one match?

_____

B. Assume that an equal number of people are born in each month.

6. If you try to guess the month someone is born in, what is the probability that you will guess the correct month?

_____

7. Suppose you are at a party with 35 people. You say that you can guarantee that you will find 2 people who were born in the same month if you can ask a certain number of people in what month he or she was born. What is the smallest number of people you can ask?

_____

MACMILLAN/McGRAW-HILL

Name _____

QUICK DRAW

Draw another figure that goes with each group.

1.

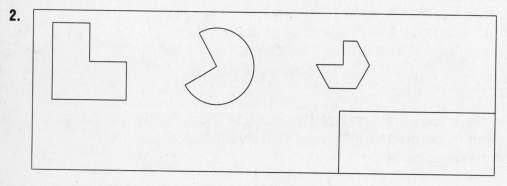

2.

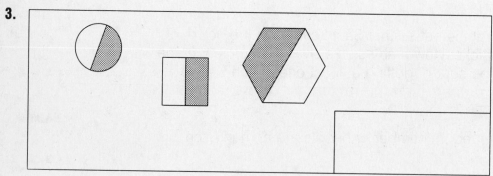

3.

MACMILLAN/McGRAW-HILL

Name _____

PROBABILITY AND PREDICTION

On Your Own   Pair and Share   In a Group

RAIN, RAIN, GO AWAY

Work with a partner. Imagine that you are the weather forecasters in a part of the country where the weather is very much the same each year. You have information about the weather for the last 50 years.

Average Number of Days of Each Type of Weather for Last 50 Years

	Jan.	Feb.	Mar.	Apr.	May	Jun.	July	Aug.	Sept.	Oct.	Nov.	Dec.
Sun	3	3	4	5	10	15	25	25	25	19	8	5
Clouds	12	10	8	15	12	13	6	5	5	10	20	16
Rain	16	15	19	10	9	2	0	1	0	2	2	10

Answer these questions from people who live in this area:

1. In which summer month should we schedule an outdoor art show? What is the probability of rain on any day of that month?

_____

2. What is the probability that it will be sunny on a day in June?

_____

3. What is the probability of either rain or clouds on a day in May?

_____

4. We want to plan school trips. What is the probability for rain on a day in September? a day in October? a day in November?

_____

5. We want to schedule a winter hike on a day when it is least likely to rain. Should we schedule it for a day in January, February, or March?

_____

6. Are we better off scheduling an outdoor event for August or September? We want the month with the highest probability of a sunny day.

_____

MACMILLAN/McGRAW-HILL

Macmillan/McGraw-Hill, MATHEMATICS IN ACTION
Grade 6, Chapter 12, Lesson 4, pages 480–481

MAKING PREDICTIONS

On Your Own   Pair and Share   In a Group

IT'S ONLY A GAME

Work with a group of friends on this activity. Imagine that you are
in charge of making new rules for a game at the school carnival.
Last year, the game was played with these rules.

RULES OF PLAY

COST OF A TURN: 4 tickets
PRIZES: If the wheel stops on 2, you win 4 tickets.

Many people did not like this game. You can find out why by
analyzing the game this way.

Think: What is the probability of winning each time? _____

How many times are you likely to win out of 10 tries? _____

How many tickets would you spend? _____

How many tickets would you win? _____

People complained that this game wasn't fair. Why do you think they felt this way?

_____

Here are some suggestions for new rules. How would a player do
in 10 tries with each set of rules?

COST: 2 tickets **PRIZE:** If the wheel stops on 2—win 4 tickets. Tickets spent: _____ Tickets won: _____	**COST:** 2 tickets **PRIZE:** If the wheel stops on even number—win 4 tickets. Tickets spent: _____ Tickets won: _____	**COST:** 1 ticket **PRIZE:** If the wheel stops on 3—win 10 tickets. Tickets spent: _____ Tickets won: _____

Now make up new rules. List your rules here. Tell why you would use these rules.

_____

_____

_____

MACMILLAN/McGRAW-HILL

Name

TRUE BLUE

The words *all, some,* or *no* (*none*) can be used to tell how two groups are related. Consider the following sentences:

> All sparrows are birds.
> Some birds are sparrows.
> Some birds are not sparrows.
> No birds are fish.

Notice that a sparrow is always a bird, but a bird is not always a sparrow (for example, a bird may be a robin). A bird is never a fish.

Write *true* or *false* for each statement.

1. All dogs are mammals. _____

2. All mammals are dogs. _____

3. Some mammals are dogs. _____

4. No tables are mammals. _____

5. All squares are quadrilaterals. _____

6. Some quadrilaterals are not squares. _____

7. Some squares are not polygons. _____

8. All numbers greater than 40 are numbers greater than 30. _____

9. Some numbers greater than 30 are numbers greater than 40. _____

10. No even numbers are odd numbers. _____

11. No odd numbers are numbers greater than 40. _____

12. Some even numbers are not numbers that end in 0, 2, 4, 6, or 8. _____

MACMILLAN/McGRAW-HILL

PROBLEM SOLVING

On Your Own   Pair and Share   In a Group

TIME OUT

The circular clock face has been used since the thirteenth century. We are all accustomed to it, but it isn't necessarily the ideal way to show time!

For example, a day has 24 hours, but a traditional clock shows only 12 hours. The hour hand on the clock has to revolve twice to show a complete 24-hour period.

Also, there are 60 minutes in an hour, but on a traditional clock the numbers 1 to 12 mark off those 60 minutes.

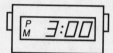 

Work with a team to try to design a better clock face. You don't have to stick to the usual clock with numbers and hands. You can invent a new way of telling time. Brainstorm to come up with ways to do some or all of these on your clock.

- show all 24 hours
- show 60 minutes in an hour
- show 60 seconds in a minute
- show whether it is night or day

Describe your group's two best ideas below. Explain how each clock works and how you use it to tell time.

Clock 1: _____

_____

Clock 2: _____

_____

MACMILLAN/McGRAW-HILL

Name _____

LISTING OUTCOMES

On Your Own   Pair and Share   In a Group

CHOW TIME!

Work with some friends to solve the problems below. There are four basic food groups:

- milk, cheese, butter
- vegetables and fruit
- poultry, meat, eggs, fish
- breads, cereals, crackers, pasta

A balanced diet should include something from each group.

1. Imagine that your committee is in charge of planning school lunches. Decide on 2 or 3 different foods to offer in each group. Next, make a tree diagram to show all the possible combinations of the foods you are offering. (Include one item from each of the four groups in each combination.)

2. Finally, go through the different combinations. Which do you think students will like the most? Pick four different complete choices. Write them here on your list of today's meals.

MONDAY'S LUNCH
1.
2.
3.
4.

MACMILLAN/McGRAW-HILL

PROBABILITY OF INDEPENDENT EVENTS

On Your Own   Pair and Share   In a Group

AND THE WINNER IS . . .

Work with a partner to solve the problems below. Sabrina and Mark are playing a game using 2 number cubes. Each is numbered 1 to 6. A player throws both cubes, computes the sum, and moves that number of spaces. Players move around a board, collecting tokens if they can land on the right squares. The player with the most tokens wins.

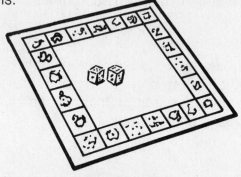

1. How many different throws are possible with 2 number cubes? (A throw of (1, 2) is different than (2, 1), for example.)

   _____

2. How many different sums are possible? What are they?

   _____

3. How many different ways can you get each sum? Make a table.

4. Sabrina is 2 squares away from a square where she can get a token. What is the probability that she will throw a 2?

   _____

5. Mark is 4 squares away from a square where he can get a token. What is the probability that he will throw a 4?

   _____

6. Sabrina lands on a square that says "You can throw the number cubes again. If you get a sum greater than 4, you win 2 tokens. If you get a sum of 4 or less, you lose a token." Should she throw the number cubes? Why or why not?

   _____

MACMILLAN/McGRAW-HILL

Name

PROBLEM SOLVING

On Your Own   **Pair and Share**   **In a Group**

IT WORKS LIKE MAGIC

In a magic square, the sum of each row, column, and diagonal is the same. For example, here the sum is 150.

80	10	60
30	50	70
40	90	20

1. Look at the magic squares below. What do these squares and the one above have in common? (*Hint:* Think about simpler numbers.)

24	3	18
9	15	21
12	27	6

$2\frac{2}{3}$	$\frac{1}{3}$	$\frac{6}{3}$
1	$1\frac{2}{3}$	$2\frac{1}{3}$
$1\frac{1}{3}$	3	$\frac{2}{3}$

2. Now use the same pattern to make two more magic squares.

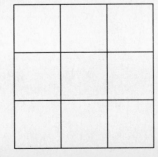

MACMILLAN/McGRAW-HILL

Macmillan/McGraw-Hill, **MATHEMATICS IN ACTION**
Grade 6, Chapter 12, Lesson 12, pages 496–497

INTEGERS AND THE NUMBER LINE

On Your Own   Pair and Share   In a Group

OPPOSITES ATTRACT

Work with a group of friends. Imagine that you are the rulers of Equaland. In Equaland, everything must stay the same. Each day you receive a report from the royal computer about the treasury, the grain stockpile, and students in the schools.

Treasury—a positive integer means tax money brought in; a negative integer means money spent from the tax money.

Grain—a positive integer means harvested bushels; a negative integer means bushels exported.

Students—a positive integer means students who enrolled in school; a negative integer means students who graduated.

Each day give your orders. *Order the opposite of everything.* Your order should look like this:

$$(-100, +600, -50)$$

The first number tells what to do with the treasury; the second number tells about grain; the third, about students. So the example means "Spend $100, harvest 600 bushels, and graduate 50 students."

1. $(+1{,}000, -200, +10)$ Tax $1,000, export 200 bushels, _____

2. $(-200, +300, +20)$ _____

3. $(+2{,}500, +150, -2)$ _____

4. $(-500, -50, +3)$ _____

Here are some reports. Write your orders for the day.

5. We raised $400 in taxes, harvested 800 bushels, and enrolled

   4 students. _____

6. We spent $1,000, exported 100 bushels, and graduated

   10 students. _____

7. We exported 200 bushels, spent $500, and enrolled 3 students. _____

8. We graduated 10 students, taxed $600, and harvested 80 bushels. _____

MACMILLAN/McGRAW-HILL

Name _____

COMPARING AND ORDERING INTEGERS

On Your Own   Pair and Share   In a Group

ORDERING FAST FOOD

Work with a friend. Put each set of integers in order from least to greatest. Under each integer, write the letter that goes with each one. You'll unscramble the name of something to eat.

1. 0   +1   −4   −6   +4
    L   A   A   S   D

___ ___ ___ ___ ___

2. +1   −3   +2   +3   −2
    Z   P   Z   A   I

___ ___ ___ ___ ___

3. +6   +1   −10   −3   −5   +9
    R   U   Y   G   O   T

___ ___ ___ ___ ___ ___

4. +1   +24   −23   −10   −3   0   +26   +30   −21
    R   G   H   M   B   U   E   R   A

___ ___ ___ ___ ___ ___ ___ ___ ___

5. −12   +9   −9   +10   −14   +13   −11   −15
    M   A   N   D   E   E   O   L

___ ___ ___ ___ ___ ___ ___ ___

6. +9   +6   −8   −7   0   −4   +1
    T   R   D   E   S   S   E

___ ___ ___ ___ ___ ___ ___

7. Now try making up some integer scrambles of your own. Exchange problems with your friend and solve them.

MACMILLAN/McGRAW-HILL

PROBLEM SOLVING

On Your Own   Pair and Share   In a Group

HALF TRUTHS

Work with a group of friends to solve the problems below.

1. Pancho and his friends have a bag of 64 peanuts. Pancho eats half of the bag. Ardeera eats half of what Pancho ate. Elena eats half the amount Ardeera ate. Jaime eats half the amount Elena ate. Kira eats half the amount Jaime ate. Josh eats the remaining peanuts. How many peanuts does Josh eat?

   _____

2. Marilee has a diary with 88 pages in it. She fills half of the pages the first month. Then, in each of the months that follow, she uses half as many pages as the month before.

   How many pages does she write in the third month? _____

   How many pages does she have left after three months? _____

   At this rate, will she start writing on the last page by the fifth month? _____

   If not, in which month will she start it? _____

3. Jackson has $25.00 in a savings account. He takes out half the money in the first month. Then, he takes out half of the money that is left in the account each month after that. (He always rounds the amount of money he withdraws to the nearest cent.)

   How much money is in the account after four months? _____

   When will there be no money left in the account? _____

4. Josefa has a string 25 in. long. She cuts off half the string. Then she cuts off half of what is left. She keeps doing this. (She does not round any of the measurements, but always cuts off exactly half.)

   Use a calculator. How long is the string after she cuts four

   times? _____

   When will there be no string left? _____

   Explain your answer. _____
   The answer to this problem is different from the answer to problem 3, which also involves the number 25. Why? Discuss with your group.

Name

GRAPHING ORDERED PAIRS

On Your Own   Pair and Share   In a Group

NAVAL DRILL

What kind of work does a dentist do in the navy?

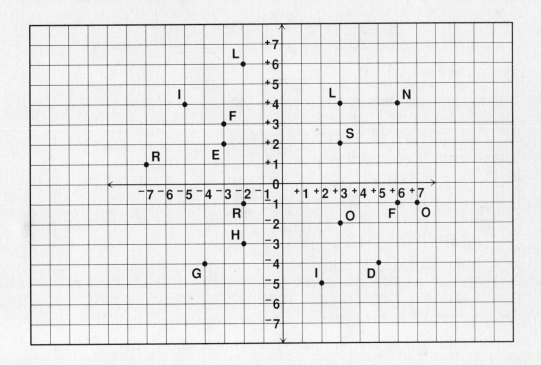

Find each of these points on the grid. Then write the letter for
each point on the lines. You'll have the answer to the question.

___ ___ ___
($^+$7, $^-$1)

___ ___ ___
($^-$3, $^+$3)

___ ___ ___
($^+$6, $^-$1)

___ ___ ___
($^+$3, $^+$2)

___ ___ ___
($^-$2, $^-$3)

___ ___ ___
($^+$3, $^-$2)

___ ___ ___
($^-$7, $^+$1)

___ ___ ___
($^-$3, $^+$2)

___ ___ ___
($^+$5, $^-$4)

___ ___ ___
($^-$2, $^-$1)

___ ___ ___
($^-$5, $^+$4)

___ ___ ___
($^-$2, $^+$6)

___ ___ ___
($^+$3, $^+$4)

___ ___ ___
($^+$2, $^-$5)

___ ___ ___
($^+$6, $^+$4)

___ ___ ___
($^-$4, $^-$4)

MACMILLAN/McGRAW-HILL

Macmillan/McGraw-Hill, MATHEMATICS IN ACTION
Grade 6, Chapter 13, Lesson 8, pages 528–529

GRAPHING TRANSFORMATIONS

On Your Own   Pair and Share   In a Group

LINE UP

1. Place each of these points on the grid below. Then connect the points.

    ($^+$2, $^-$4), ($^+$2, $^-$2), ($^+$2, $^+$1), ($^+$2, $^+$3)

2. What kind of figure do you get? _____

    In what direction does it go? _____

3. Compare the first numbers in each ordered pair. What do you

    notice about the numbers? _____

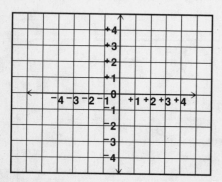

4. Name some other points that will make the same kind

    of line. _____

    Place these points on the grid.

5. What do you notice about the ordered pairs? _____
    ($^-$4, $^+$3), ($^-$2, $^+$3), ($^+$1, $^+$3), ($^+$3, $^+$3)

    What kind of figure do you get? _____

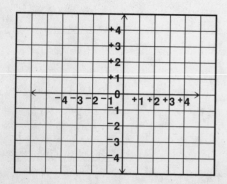

6. Name some other points that will make the same kind

    of line. _____

    Place these points on the grid.

MACMILLAN/McGRAW-HILL

Name _____

ENRICHMENT-139

PROBLEM SOLVING

On Your Own   Pair and Share   In a Group

INTERESTING ANSWERS

Work with a group to solve these problems. Let one member of the group use a calculator while the others decide what numbers should be used.

When you deposit money in a savings bank, the amount in your account is called the principal. This amount earns **interest** at a fixed rate over a period of time. Interest is calculated as follows:

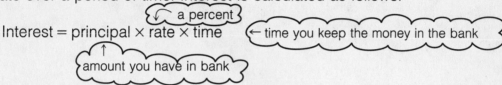

Interest = principal × rate × time   ← time you keep the money in the bank

a percent

amount you have in bank

The interest on $200 at 12% interest for 2 years is

Interest = $200 × 12% × 2 = $48

1. What is the interest earned on $1,000 at 6% interest for 3 years?

    _____

2. What is the interest on $670 at 8.5% interest for $1\frac{1}{2}$ years?

    _____

3. **a.** If you put $100 in the bank at 7% interest, how much money do you have at the end of a year?

    _____

    b. If you keep the interest in the bank, the next year the bank will pay you interest on the principal plus the interest earned in the first year. (This is called **compound interest**.) How much interest will be paid in the second year?

    _____

    c. What will your bank balance be at the end of the second year?

    _____

4. **a.** Yoni puts $100 in the bank at 8% interest. He takes the interest earned out at the end of each year. At the end of 5 years, what is the total value of the bank balance plus the interest he has withdrawn?

    _____

    b. Paco puts $100 in the same bank. He leaves the interest in the bank and gets compound interest at 8%. How much does he have in the bank after 5 years?

    _____

5. How much will Yoni have after 10 years?

    _____

6. How much will Paco have after 10 years?

    _____

Enrichment-139

Macmillan/McGraw-Hill, MATHEMATICS IN ACTION
Grade 6, Chapter 13, Lesson 10, pages 532–533